S0-BLX-295

WILDLIFE OF CALIFORNIA

By George Seymour
Supervisor of Conservation Education

State of California
The Resources Agency
Department of Fish and Game
1968

OVERSIZE
QL
164
S485

CONTENTS

1968

Prebound in "Treasure Trove" and distributed exclusively by

Perc B. Sapsis, Inc.

Seaside, California 93955

Library of Congress Catalog Card No. 68–28356

BANDTAILED PIGEON

WILDLIFE LEAFLET

State of California
DEPARTMENT OF FISH AND GAME

BAND-TAILS PREFER THE FOREST, TAKE TO THE HILLS IN SUMMER

The band-tailed pigeon gets its name from the wide blackish band that crosses the midtail. It resembles the domestic pigeon, and is easily distinguished from the dove by its broad rounded tail, and dark overall bluish color. The bill and legs are yellow and the eyelids are naked and bright red. Adults have a narrow white crescent that forms a collar at the base of the neck.

The band-tail is migratory. These pigeons live primarily in natural forests and in summer prefer high elevations. Their breeding range is mostly in the north coast range and at higher elevations on the western slopes of the Sierra Cascade Mountains. They start their northern migration as early as January and are found nesting in northern California, on north through western Oregon, Washington, and into British Columbia, arriving there by mid-May.

The courtship of the male is typical of the pigeon family: There is a display of short flights, and much cooing. After a mate is chosen they select a nest site. Nesting is usually done singly in widely scattered spots, although sometimes food conditions will draw a number of birds into a loose rookery.

The female builds a flimsy nest. In California it may be in a small shrub or in a huge Douglas fir tree. She may take a week or so to complete the nest and when finished observers wonder how it can hold an egg or a baby pigeon.

The female lays one pure white egg, rarely two. Both parents help with the incubation. In 18 to 20 days the young are hatched, naked, except for a thin coat of yellowish down. Both the mother and

ADULT BANDTAILED PIGEONS

BANDTAILED SQUAB ON A NEST

father feed the squab by regurgitating a thick whitish pigeon milk that is manufactured in glands on the walls of the pigeon's crop. After a diet of pigeon milk for one week, fruit and insects are added, and soon the baby is nearly as large as its parents. By the 30th day it is full feathered and ready to fly. In California marked pairs of pigeons have been observed rearing two broods, using the same nest. Sometimes the pigeons brood only one egg each year. In the fall they start their southern migration. Most of the migrating flocks range in numbers from 10 to 40, although some years see them in bands of hundreds to thousands. Their migratory habits are so erratic that it is hard to predict when or where they will appear next. If food is plentiful they dally along the way. When food is scarce they travel hundreds of miles and appear suddenly in a good food area in flocks of thousands. Normally it takes about three months for them to reach southern California in the fall flight.

When not actually migrating their daily habits are roosting and feeding. They generally roost at high elevations. At daybreak the large roosting flocks break up into smaller groups and swoop down to lower elevations to feed. The morning flight may take them to a hillside of madrone berries, or to a farmer's harvested grain field. Usually by 9 or 10 o'clock the feeding period is over and they spiral upwards to return to roost in the tall trees at higher elevations. They sit quietly through the day and repeat the feeding activity from 4 o'clock in the afternoon till dark.

The pigeons are seed and fruit eaters. Acorns make up the bulk of their diet. They prefer the acorns of the blue oak and California live oak. They eat the fruits of dogwood, madrone and cascara. When feeding on cascara the flesh takes on a slightly bitter taste. It is interesting to watch them feed on manzanita blossoms in the spring. The slender twigs bend with the weight of the bird, which will execute all sorts of acrobatics while holding on and trying to eat at the same time.

Occasionally great flocks descend on farm crops and cause damage. They eat prunes, cherries, and sprouting grains. When food is plentiful they become widely scattered and their crop depredations go practically unnoticed.

The pigeon is protected as a migratory game bird. Because of its erratic habits fewer hunters pursue it, making it appear a game bird of lesser importance. Normally the limited hunting that is afforded by the short season and the bird's presence, has little effect on pigeon populations. It is a fast flyer, and difficult to kill. To the hunter who has studied the birds, and is free to go when it appears, the pigeon offers a fast elusive target. Properly prepared, it is a delight on the table. The band-tail's habits, and controlled hunting seasons and limits make it possible to maintain this species for everyone to enjoy.

California Wildlife Information Sheet

The Resources Agency of California—Department of Fish and Game

Bear

Of all the large mammals in the mountain forests of California, the black bear is one of the most interesting.

Today the black bear is the only bear in the State. Before 1922, California was also the home of the grizzly bear. The grizzly was larger than the black bear and quite ferocious. The early settlers found that they and the grizzly could not live in peace because it killed their livestock and even bothered the settlers; so they set about with no thought to the future and killed them all. The last grizzly bear was killed in 1922 in Tulare County, leaving the black bear as the only bear in California. Later, in 1953, the State Legislature chose the now extinct California grizzly bear as the official State animal. It is the one used on California's flag.

The fur of the black bear is long and dense. It may be black, dark brown, cinnamon brown, yellowish brown, and sometimes bluish in color. The largest black bear of which there is an official record in California was live trapped in Yosemite Park. It weighed 680 pounds. Ordinarily the adult bear weighs between 200 and 300 pounds. The black bear appears rather clumsy, due to his flat footed shuffling gait, but he can move rapidly if the occasion demands. He climbs trees readily and the smaller bears usually seek safety in trees if danger threatens. Bears tend to be nocturnal and even though they sometimes move around in daylight hours they are so elusive and shy that they are seldom seen, except around parks where they have learned to seek handouts from park tourists. The park bears sometimes become very cranky and can be quite dangerous.

There are two races of black bear in California. One is called the northwestern black bear and is found in California's northwestern counties. The other is the Sierra Nevada black bear. It lives in the Sierra Nevada Mountains and its range extends south to Kern County and then west into parts of the Coast Range mountains. The black bear occupies a rather small area in the forest, but it does wander with the seasons as different food becomes available. Normally, the black bear does not prey on game or domestic livestock but occasionally one will kill a hog, sheep, calf, or fawn. Because they

Photo by Wyoming Fish and Game Department

BLACK BEAR

are carrion eaters and may be seen eating the remains of an animal that died of other causes, they are sometimes falsely accused.

In winter in the southern parts of the State and at lower elevations in the mountains, the weather is so mild that the bear does not go into true hibernation. In colder areas and at higher elevations it does den up and sleep for long periods of time. The young are born during this dormant period, usually in January. They are very small, weighing only six or eight ounces, and are blind and helpless for 30 or 40 days. They grow slowly at first but by the time mother is ready to leave the den in May they are usually well developed and are about 18 inches long. The first young of a three-year-old female is usually a single cub, but twins and triplets are common after that.

Young bears are very appealing as babies, but no attempt should be made to capture them. First, because it is illegal, and, secondly, a mother bear with cubs is dangerous and the cubs grow so rapidly they do not make good pets anyway.

Bears are omnivorous in their feeding habits. They eat different things they find in the woods. In the spring when they waken from their winter sleep they eat fresh green vegetation like skunk cabbage, grasses, and the tender buds of sprouting trees. Through the summer and fall they eat berries, insects, fruits, carrion, acorns, fish and honey. They tear open wild nests of honey with their sharp claws and sometimes, if stands of bee hives have been set up in the forest, without the protection of an electric fence, the bears destroy the hives and eat the bees and honey. In areas where bears are overabundant they may also turn to eating the inner bark of trees, thus doing some damage to second-growth timber.

The bear has been a prized game animal in many states for years, but has not been hunted extensively in California. Even with the present increased hunting effort, the black bear has held its own and has flourished in certain parts of its range. Because reproduction is slow, care is taken to make certain that hunters do not take too many each year, because we do not want the black bear to become extinct like the grizzly.

Photo by U.S. Fish and Wildlife Service MOTHER BEAR AND CUBS

California Wildlife Information Sheet

The Resources Agency of California—Department of Fish and Game

Beaver

The beaver is the largest member of the rodent family in North America. It is the only wild animal that actually changes its environment to suit its needs. It cuts trees, both large and small, and builds dams to impound water in which to live. It also digs canals to transport food and building materials when the supply of trees near water is exhausted.

The beaver is a large animal. Adults average from 30 to 40 pounds each, with some individuals growing to 100 pounds. Its head is massive and its large, orange-colored incisors are well suited to gnawing. Its eyes are small and its little ears are nearly hidden in its dense fur. The beaver's body is plump and covered uniformly with rich, brown fur. Its large hind feet are webbed and it has a large, flat, hairless paddle-shaped tail.

The beaver is semiaquatic and needs a continuous supply of water in which to live, with available food nearby. Water several feet deep is required for escape to safety. Whenever a beaver chooses to live near shallow water, it builds dams to impound the water. Some of the dams may be 200 or 300 feet long and 8 feet high.

Along deep rivers and sloughs, the beavers prefer to live in dens they dig themselves in the banks along the water. They sometimes build homes or lodges in small rocky streams or shallow waters. A beaver lodge may be 15 feet across and 6 or 8 feet high. Like the dams, it is also built of limbs, mud, tules, cornstalks or other easily available materials.

The beaver always provides for its home an underwater entrance which leads up to a chamber above water level.

The beaver feeds on the bark and tender twigs of water-loving trees like willow, cottonwood and aspen, and it also likes roots, bulbs, grasses and tules.

Beavers do not hibernate, but in cold weather they stay in their homes for days, subsisting on food which they have stored. An eager beaver may come out in daylight, but for the most part, cutting and building is done at night.

Each lodge contains a family of beavers—the young of the year and the young of the previous year. When the young are approaching their second year, they are driven out to start a colony of their own. This is nature's way of dispersing this species.

The mating season commences in February and most litters are born in April and May. The mother has only one litter a year and there is an average of four kits to the litter.

This baby beaver was captured, along with a number of adults, in a transplanting operation carried out by the Department of Fish and Game. His cuteness won lots of friends on his trip, but he was happiest when he was released with his parents into his new home.

Although there is only one species of beaver, there were three geographical variations . . . the Sonora beaver along the Colorado River, the Golden beaver in Sacramento and San Joaquin Valleys, and the Shasta beaver in Northern California. They were trapped nearly to extinction by the end of the 19th century. In 1911, the season was entirely closed and for the next 35 years the season was kept closed, except for beavers that were permitted to be taken in areas where they were interfering with agriculture.

From 1945 to 1955, the Department of Fish and Game transplanted 3,000 beavers into all the suitable waters in California. Today beavers may be found in suitable waters throughout the State and up to 9,000 feet elevation in the Sierra.

The beaver ranks second in economic importance to the muskrat in the California fur trade. Approximately 1,600 beavers were reported taken in 1962-63.

Beavers far removed from agriculture still have a high esthetic value. The operations of a successful beaver colony, with its series of dams, is one of nature's wonders. In a restricted area like a small valley, beavers soon multiply beyond the carrying capacity of the valley. If they are not reduced sharply in numbers each year, they soon eat themselves out of house and home by cutting all the suitable trees, and the regrowth is utilized faster than it can be replaced. The beaver must then imigrate. When they leave the safety of their homes, beavers become subject to disease and predation, or they end up in waters that are being used by man. Their depredations cause them to be looked upon by agriculturists as undesirable rodents. This whole cycle takes place in a few short years.

STATE OF CALIFORNIA • THE RESOURCES AGENCY • DEPARTMENT OF FISH AND GAME

California Wildlife Information Sheet
The Resources Agency of California—Department of Fish and Game

Bighorn Sheep

The bighorn sheep is California's most remarkable big game animal. It has a special appeal to nature lovers and outdoorsmen because, like the mountain goat and the caribou of Alaska, it is truly a wilderness species.

There are only a few places in California where bighorn may be viewed from the roadside, but they can still be found if the person is willing to hike into the isolated and, by human standards, inhospitable places where they prefer to live.

Widely distributed over the western hemisphere, it is estimated that there are still between 2,000 and 2,500 of these splendid animals in California. They are scattered in bands, high along the west side of Owens Valley, on the eastern slopes of the Sierra Nevada, and from the White Mountains in Mono County south to Mexico. Small bands may be found throughout the deserts of Southern California. The high forbidding peaks of the San Gabriels, within 50 miles of the heart of Los Angeles, still have a remnant population to delight the hardiest naturalist.

Both the male and female bighorn grow horns that are never shed. The growth rings indicate the animal's age. The ewe's horns are flat, slightly curved, and only 8 or 10 inches long. The ram's horns look about the same till he is two years old. After this age they begin to grow larger until they become massive, round, full curl. The head and horns of an adult ram may weigh 31 or 32 pounds. With increasing age, the bighorn sheep tend to rub the horn ends to a blunt tip. The coat of a bighorn sheep is not woolly but more the texture and color of deer hair, and is darker on the rams.

Bighorn sheep separate and live in ram bands and ewe bands most of the year. They gather together during the breeding season, which in California extends from October to December.

During the breeding season the rams fight for possession of the ewes. They do not choose a single mate. A fight between two adult rams is a spectacle not soon forgotten. Facing each other, sometimes 20 or 30 feet apart, they rear and charge in almost a stately jousting match, crashing their massive horns together, time after time, until one or the other retires.

BIGHORN SHEEP RAM AND EWE

DFG Photo by Bonnar Blong

BIGHORN SHEEP

The females breed at 18 months and the single lambs are born in 180 days. The lambs start tasting different things in a few days and are completely weaned in four or five months. The bighorn sheep feed on various kinds of grasses, leafy weeds, and shrubs. They are able to utilize the moisture of their food. If their food has lots of moisture, they may range 20 miles from water. In the hot, dry months they come to water twice a week, more often if water is near.

The bighorn sheep has been entirely protected in California since 1873 but the specialized requirements of these animals have placed a strict limit on their increase or spread to other ranges. The present population remains about the same.

Even through given year-round protection, they disappeared from Northern California as early as 1920. Many reasons have been advanced for their decline but the main ones were overgrazing by livestock, the introduction of diseases from livestock, principally from domestic sheep, and the rapid increase of human activity such as building roads, illegal hunting, and the appropriation of water. Even some springs a long way from settlements were boxed in and the water piped away.

Water seems to be the main thing that limits the number of bighorn sheep in an area.

Because there is so much interest in the bighorn, by both the sportsmen and the nature lovers, the Department of Fish and Game has made extensive water developments in areas that are suitable. Under proper management and protection in the dry and formidable places they have chosen to live, the bighorn should be with us for years to come.

YOUNG BIGHORN RAM

U.S. Fish and Wildlife Service Photo

California Wildlife Information Sheet

The Resources Agency of California—Department of Fish and Game

Bobcat

There is only one species of bobcat. In California geographic variations have some effect on the color of bobcats. Those found in timber and heavy brush fields are quite spotted, while those found in the deserts of northeastern California are more of a pale tawny gray, with a complete absence of spots on the back and all markings are less bold. The bobcat has long legs and large paws. Large specimens can weigh up to 30 pounds.

Its name may have originated from its short tail, which is only six or seven inches long. The end of its tail is always black tipped with white, which distinguishes the bobcat from its northern cousin, the Canadian lynx, whose tail is tipped solid black.

Food Habits

Despite its pussycat appearance when seen in repose, the bobcat is quite fierce and is equipped to kill animals as large as deer. When living near a ranch it may take lambs, poultry, and even young pigs. However, food habit studies have shown the major part of its diet is made up of rabbits, ground squirrels, mice, pocket gophers, and wood rats. Quail have been found in bobcat stomachs but predation by bobcats does not harm healthy game populations.

The bobcat roams freely at night, early in the morning, and in the evening; and occasionally travels abroad during the daytime. It does not dig its own den. If a crevice or a cave is not available, it will den in a dense thicket of brush or sometimes choose a hollow in a log or a tree. Each bobcat occupies a fairly small area in the forest and seldom hunts more than a mile from its home range.

The bobcat's growls and snarls are so deep and fearsome, particularly when hidden from view, that one gets the illusion it must be a mountain lion. Its mating behavior is similar to a housecat's. The young are born any time in spring or summer with the most litters arriving in April and May. Litters average three kittens. The kittens are born blind and are completely dependent on their mother for several months. With skill and patience a bobcat kitten can be tamed and makes an interesting pet, but is inclined to be a "one-man" animal. As bobcats reach two years of age they are

YOUNG BOBCAT

Photo by U.S. Fish and Wildlife Service

New Mexico Dept. of Game and Fish

BOBCAT PORTRAITS

U.S. Forest Service

apt to get grouchy and dangerous and then should be kept alone and away from strangers.

Range

The bobcat has the widest and most continuous range of any carnivore in California and, except for metropolitan areas, is found in all mountain areas. Where it is found it shows a decided preference for rocky, bushy hillsides in which to live and hunt.

Thoughtless people still shoot a bobcat on sight, considering it a heartless killer of game and livestock, despite food habit studies that have shown that a major portion of its diet is made up of destructive rodents. When an individual animal preys on poultry and the young of livestock it should be destroyed to protect the farmer or rancher.

The bobcat's coat in wintertime is a desirable fur. The popularity of bobcat fur runs in cycles of 10 to 15 years. It is fashionable at present and is in demand. Because of the mixed feelings about its predatory habits, it is nonprotected and may be taken at any time. However, in remote areas where there is no conflict with livestock, bobcats should be taken only in the winter months when the dense silky fur is at its best. Commercial trappers trap and sell from 300 to 500 each year. Some of the pelts are used as rugs or wall hangings but most of them are used as trim on cloth coats.

BOBCAT

CALIFORNIA CONDOR

WILDLIFE LEAFLET

State of California
DEPARTMENT OF FISH AND GAME

THE CONDOR CONTINUES A DWINDLING EXISTENCE IN THE RUGGED HILLS OF THE SOUTHLAND

The condor has the largest wingspread of any land bird in North America. Within the time of pioneers in California these huge birds roamed the skies of western North America and South America. Today only two widely separated species remain: the Andean condor, which lives in South América, and the California condor which has continued a passive but dwindling existence in its last stronghold in the rugged mountains of Ventura and Santa Barbara Counties in California.

Attaining a weight of about 20 pounds and a wingspread of nine feet, these remarkable creatures are a lingering relic of the ice age; a cousin of sorts to a vulturelike bird that lived with the saber-toothed tiger and the mastodon years ago.

The fully mature condor somewhat resembles the turkey vulture, but is more than twice as large and much broader in proportion. It has a long featherless neck, and a bald head that is pinkish orange. The eyes are bright red. When perched, the body appears to be covered with a coat of black feathers, except for a prominent white wing bar. When flying, the broad white feathers along the entire forward part of the underwing are exposed. This is a distinctive mark of the adult condor. Generally, young birds appear all black. Condors alight, walk, and take off in a laborious manner, but once airborne they excel in soaring and flying long distances. Riding the air currents on immense wings like a glider, they may range out 100 miles or more from their home in constant search for food.

The condors, like other vultures, do not kill their food. They live entirely on carrion—from dead animals the size of a squirrel up to the remains of a steer. After gorging themselves they return home to feed their young or to roost silently on a tree snag or a ledge of rock close by.

They do not make a nest but choose a place in some inaccessible area. It might be a hollow in a

Photo by U. S. Fish and Wildlife Service

big tree or a cave or just a cleft in the face of a rocky ledge. They do not breed until they are five or six years old. The female lays only one egg every two years. The egg is pale green, about 4½ inches long. It is hatched in from 42 to 45 days. People think the chick is very homely. It is snow white at first and then later changes to grayish brown. It is brooded and fed for five months before it leaves the nest. The young condor, still dependent on its parents, continues to roost and make short flights around the nest for another nine months before it is able to fend for itself. Studies have indicated that during the nesting period human intrusion even to within one-half mile may cause the parent birds to quietly abandon the nest for hours, exposing the eggs and the young to the weather and to hunger, which could cause death.

Early explorers found the condor inhabiting the mountain ranges from Lower California to Oregon. By the turn of the century civilization was pressing in and their numbers declined until only a few remained in the rugged mountains of southern California. Many things contributed to their steady decline. They were shot for the feathers; the quills from the great flight feathers were used as containers for gold dust by the early miners. They were killed by the curious just to be examined and discarded, and the eggs and feathers were sought by collectors. Less obvious reasons have been the birds' slow rate of reproduction and the general intrusion of man's activities into their range.

In 1901 thoughtful men realized that the condor was disappearing and passed laws protecting it as a nongame bird. But their numbers continued to dwindle.

An exhaustive study completed by the National Audubon Society and the University of California in the late nineteen forties estimated at that time that there were only 60 condors left in California. A more recent study by the same two agencies completed in 1964 estimates their number to be about 40.

The California Department of Fish and Game in 1965 conducted the first of a series of annual counts with the cooperation of the National Audubon Society, the University of California, the U.S. Bureau of Sport Fisheries and Wildlife, and the U.S. Forest Service. In this count, 38 birds were observed.

At present two sanctuaries are set aside primarily for the protection of nesting, roosting, and resting areas for the condors.

The Sisquoc area was established by the Forest Service in 1937 in Santa Barbara County. The larger and more important Sespe Wildlife Area, some 53,000 acres, was established by the same agency in Ventura County in 1947 and expanded to its present size in 1951. Both areas are within the Los Padres National Forest and are closed to public use, and now both state and federal laws protect the condors.

The National Audubon Society, the U.S. Bureau of Sport Fisheries and Wildlife, the U.S. Forest Service, and the Department of Fish and Game, as well as other interested agencies and individuals, are gravely concerned for the welfare of these great birds. Despite the fact that the disruptive forces of man are rapidly altering the ecology of the condor, the combined efforts of these people are directed toward finding some means for its perpetuation.

The condor, harmless to man and beast, is a living part of California's heritage. Due to its great rarity and scientific interest, observers wait and watch patiently for a glimpse of its soaring beauty, and almost everyone experiences a feeling of exultance when a condor is seen to wheel and dip in magnificent flight.

California Wildlife Information Sheet

The Resources Agency of California—Department of Fish and Game

Canada Goose

Canada geese are interesting for within their numerous subspecies are found the largest and smallest members of the goose family.

Four of the Canada subspecies may be found in California. They all have long, thin, black necks; the head is black with white cheek patches, and the bill and feet are black. The general appearance is the same in color and markings. The main difference is in their size. The two biggest species because of their clarion cry are often called Canadian honkers.

The largest, the Great Basin Canada goose, is the only one that also breeds and lives in northeastern California and normally spends the winters in the valleys in central California. The Great Basin Canada that winters in Imperial Valley migrates down the east side of the Sierras from its breeding grounds in northern states and Canada. It is a large bird, weighing from 8 to 14 pounds, with a wingspread of 5 to 6 feet.

The other three migrate to California from their Canadian and Alaskan breeding grounds. The Western Canada is a little smaller than the Great Basin Canada goose. It comes to California down the west coast as far south as Del Norte and Humboldt Counties. The Lesser Canada, which weighs from 5 to 6 pounds, and the Cackling Goose or Cackler, which only weighs from 2½ to 3½ pounds, both winter in great numbers in the valleys of central California. The little Cackler is the only Canada goose that winters exclusively in California.

The larger forms are easily recognized by their great size and their voice. Their voice is a clear resonant *ah-honk* with a break between syllables. The smaller ones have a higher pitched voice and they call much faster in a cackling way. They all have a variety of conversational notes or "goose talk" both in the air and on the ground. When traveling far, they fly fast with measured, regular wing beats, calling frequently in a trumpeting clangorous voice that has stirred excitement in man since early times.

The Canada geese graze in open fields and are normally day feeders. They walk and swim without effort, showing more preference for water during the breeding season.

The first signs of spring fill the wild geese with a restless impulse to be gone. They congregate in flocks and express their uneasiness with much gabbling and honking as though discussing the long

GREAT BASIN CANADA GOOSE *Photo by Colorado Game & Fish Dept.*

CACKLER ON LEFT

GOSLINGS SIMILAR FOR BOTH

WESTERN CANADA ON RIGHT

trip ahead. The big honkers are the first to leave the wintering grounds.

Some of the Great Basin Canadas, on their return north, stay in northeastern California marshes and reservoirs. They build their large, rather bulky nest near water in a variety of places: on banks, little islands, on top of muskrat houses, and in the tops of old dead trees. Some of them readily accept artificial nesting platforms installed by Fish and Game personnel.

The goose lays from 4 to 10 (usually 5 or 6) creamy white eggs. The young are hatched by the goose, in from 25 to 30 days. It is doubtful that the gander ever sits on the eggs but he does remain in close attendance, ready to protect the nest from danger. The baby geese are called goslings. After the eggs are hatched both the goose and the gander guard the goslings carefully. The family almost immediately seeks cover at the water's edge at this time, for protection, for soon after the young are hatched the adults' annual moult takes place, leaving them also flightless for several weeks. Many families of geese congregate at this time. The family is close knit and remains together for their first year.

Geese are long lived. There are records of geese nearly 50 years old that breed regularly. Great ability is shown by some of the older birds in leading the flocks on the long routes to and from the wintering grounds. Long prized as a table bird, the Canada goose tests the skill of experienced hunters and the Great Basin honker is the trophy bird of them all.

The establishment of wildlife management areas along the migratory routes, and the carefully regulated hunting seasons and bag limits have made it possible for these great birds to survive and even increase, therefore, even today in both spring and fall, one may see long lines of geese lace the sky, and at night who doesn't thrill to the trumpeting call of the honker as he leads his flock across a trackless sky?

GREAT BASIN CANADA

LESSER CANADA

CHUKAR PARTRIDGE

WILDLIFE LEAFLET

State of California
DEPARTMENT OF FISH AND GAME

A NATIVE OF THE MEDITERRANEAN, THE CHUKAR HAS TAKEN TO CALIFORNIA

THE COLORFUL AND EXCITING CHUKAR, a member of the red-legged partridge family, has rapidly been gaining favor with the sportsmen in California since the first limited hunting season on chukars was opened in 1954. Red-legged partridges are native to countries around the Mediterranean Sea and most of the south half of Asia. An Indian strain, commonly called the chukar, was introduced into California in 1932 from stock purchased in India. In the following years until 1955 over 52,000 chukars were released from state game farms in different parts of the state, but it was only in the high desert type country of eastern and south central California that the chukar flourished.

The chukar is a plump bird nearly three times as large as a quail. The male and female look alike. The markings are distinctive. It has a white throat patch edged in black, and the sides are barred with black and white in sharp contrast to the pale brownish gray of the breast and back. The beak and legs of the mature bird are bright red.

The chukar roosts and nests on the ground. It lives in large flocks or coveys. Wintering coveys break up and pair in February. The nesting season lasts from May until August. The hen lays from 7 to 16 fairly sharp-pointed eggs that vary in color from yellowish white to brownish cream, and are speckled with purplish to reddish brown spots. The young are ready to leave the nest as soon as the last chick hatched is dry. The young are not capable of flight for two weeks. During this period if the young are endangered the mother

RED-LEGGED PARTRIDGE

pretends injury and flutters away crying in a piteous manner to decoy the enemy away from her brood.

The young birds eat numerous insects. As they grow older they eat the seeds, leaves, and stems of grasses and plants as well as the seeds and fruits of some shrubs.

Chukars are limited in their range by the availability of water. During hot, dry summer months they are seldom found more than a mile from water. However, as soon as the annual rains start, the coveys scatter over a wide area.

When a covey is flushed they burst from the ground on powerful wings. If their flight is downhill, they fly very fast. When they land they usually run uphill, and the hunter without a dog is sorely pressed to keep within shooting range. However, soon after a flock is scattered they begin to call in a clear, ringing note that can be heard a long distance in the quiet desert air.

Other red-legged partridges are being studied by the Department of Fish and Game. The most important so far, of course, is the Indian chukar. Although well established now in rough, semiarid mountains in many parts of the state, it has not proven adaptable to California's wetter coastal counties.

In a carefully planned experiment the French and Spanish red-legged partridge, the Barbary partridge, and the Turkish and Greek chukars, have been planted more recently in a program to expand the range of the red-legged partridges in the state. They all have the same general size and appearance of the Indian chukar, except the border of the throat patch of the French, Spanish, and Barbary red-legged partridge is a mottled reddish brown.

BARBARY

FRENCH AND SPANISH RED-LEGGED PARTRIDGE

CHUKAR

The particular requirements of each species has been studied and they are being planted in areas that are suitable for their needs and where there will be no competition with native game birds. Nearly 12,000 birds of these varieties have been released since 1958.

The season has not been opened yet in the counties in which this program is being conducted. However, if these varieties of partridge do as well in their new environment as their cousin, the Indian chukar, the call and hurtling flight of California's newest introduction will be a source of pleasure to the hunter and bird lover statewide.

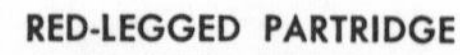

RED-LEGGED PARTRIDGE

COTTONTAIL

WILDLIFE LEAFLET

State of California
DEPARTMENT OF FISH AND GAME

POPULAR AND PROLIFIC, THE COTTONTAIL IS AS CUTE AS A BUNNY

The cottontail rabbit is perhaps the best known and most widely hunted small game animal in the United States. Subspecies and geographical variations can be found coast to coast and in California from sea level to high mountain elevations.

In California there are four cottontails—the Audubon cottontail, Nuttall cottontail, brush rabbit, and pygmy rabbit. The pygmy rabbit is of least importance because of its scarcity and the fact that it lives at high elevations in remote areas in eastern and northeastern California.

The cottontails are true rabbits. They all have one thing in common, which makes them different from the jackrabbits or hares. The cottontails build a nest, and their babies are born naked with their eyes closed, whereas the true hares do not build a nest, and their babies are born fully furred with their eyes open. The gestation period is from 26 to 30 days. There may be as many as three litters of from two to six babies born each year. The cottontail digs a shallow hole and lines it with the soft downy fur which she plucks from her own chest. She crouches over the nest while the babies nurse. When she leaves the nest to feed, she carefully covers the babies completely with fur. About a week after birth the young open their eyes and commence to nibble on grass. Soon the babies are eating the same things as their mother which is usually grass, leaves of various plants, fallen fruits, and sometimes acorns. They rarely eat the bark of trees or shrubs.

Cottontails are light leapers

The Nuttall cottontail lives in the brushy, rocky places in the sagebrush country, generally on the east side of the Sierra-Cascade crest.

The Audubon cottontail is the most common and is found in the lowlands of California and occasionally ranging up into the low foothills on either side of the Sacramento and San Joaquin Valley.

The little brush rabbit inhabits the dense brushlands of the hills and mountainous areas in the western half of California from Oregon clear to the Mexican border.

California hunters do not attach as much importance to rabbit hunting as do hunters in some eastern states. Here, the cottontails are usually hunted in conjunction with other game. However, there is evidence of increasing interest. In 1963 it was estimated that nearly three-fourths of a million cottontails were taken by California hunters. A brace of cottontail rabbits is a welcome addition to the quail or pheasant hunter's bag, and fried cottontail, biscuits and gravy is the reward for those skillful enough to bag the gray little speedster with the white fluff of a tail, as he races, bobbing and darting through dense cover.

The pigmy cottontail

The Resources Agency of California—Department of Fish and Game

Coyote

The coyote, or "little wolf" as it was called by the Indians, is found in all life zones in California from the floors of the valleys to the tops of the mountains. It is a member of the dog family. In size and shape it's like a medium-sized shepherd dog, but its tail is round and bushy and is carried straight out and below the level of its back.

Coyotes found in the low deserts and valleys are a grayish tawny brown with a black tip on the tail. At high elevations and on the east side of the Sierra the color is more gray and the underparts are nearly white. Some specimens have a white tip on their tail. In wintertime their coat becomes long and silky. Trappers then hunt them for their fur.

●

The coyote is one of the few wild animals whose voice is commonly heard. Coyotes howl at night and their voice is made up of a high quavering cry, and crazy, high-pitched yappings. Sometimes, when it is first heard, the listener may experience a tingling of man's fear of primitive danger, but to the outdoorsman it is truly a song of the West.

The coyote usually digs its own den, although sometimes it will enlarge an old badger hole, or maybe just fix up a natural hole in a rocky ledge to suit its own needs. The dens are usually hidden from view, but are fairly easy to locate because of the trails which lead away from the den.

The mother coyote has one litter of puppies a year. The gestation period is from 63 to 65 days. They have from three to nine pups to the litter, and most litters are born in April and May.

●

The male does little to support the family. He will bring food fairly close, but the mother does not allow him to come all the way to the den. The pups live in the den and play near the entrance until they are about 10 weeks old. Then the mother starts taking them out hunting in a group. They gradually break up, and by fall the pups are usually hunting alone.

The crafty coyote can be seen almost anywhere in California. This one was trotting along a road in the early morning and paused to look the photographer over before moving on. DFG photo by Jim Ruch.

The coyote does not hibernate. It travels over a wide range and hunts both day and night. It runs swiftly and easily captures its prey. It has a varied diet and seems able to exist on whatever the area offers in the way of food. It has been seen killing deer, sheep, and poultry. It eats meat and fish, fresh or spoiled. At times it eats fruits and vegetable matter, and has been known to raid melon patches. However, rabbits, ground squirrels, small rodents, insects and reptiles make up the greater part of its diet.

The coyote is found in every California county except San Francisco, and is still seen occasionally in the suburban areas of some of California's largest cities. It is common in most rural areas.

Some livestockmen and sportsmen feel that the coyote should be exterminated, as were the grizzly bear and the wolf. Biologists agree that individual animals that are killing domestic stock or poultry should be destroyed, but that the species as a whole is not necessarily harmful, because so much of its diet is made up of destructive rodents.

Coyotes are nonprotected and can be taken at any time. It is interesting to note that, despite constant hunting and many efforts to reduce the coyote population, on a quiet night the song of "El Coyote" may still be heard in most parts of California.

California Wildlife Information Sheet

The Resources Agency of California—Department of Fish and Game

Deer

Almost everyone is familiar with the deer, for it is the most common and widespread of California's big game animals. Few persons, even deer hunters, know that the native deer are all mule deer and that they all belong to the mule deer species. The large size of their ears was the source of the name mule deer.

All the deer in California have many characteristics in common. They are primarily browsing animals. They eat the twigs, buds and leaves of shrubs and trees, and acorns in the fall. In early spring and late fall they "graze" on green grasses and leafy plants.

They all tend to be migratory except along the coast and in the southern desert areas where snows do not drive them to a winter range.

The deer's keenest sense is its hearing. It has rather poor vision for stationary objects but is quick to catch motion—particularly the appearance of a strange silhouette on the skyline.

Both the bucks and the does have reddish summer coats which are replaced to gray in the fall as the long hairs grow out to form their winter coats.

The bucks alone have antlers, which are shed each year in midwinter. The bucks are bareheaded until a new set starts to grow in the spring. They grow rapidly, and while growing are covered with a velvetlike skin which is rubbed off as soon as the antlers harden in the fall.

Normally a mature buck has four points on each antler. The number of points is not an indicator of age, for the quality and quantity of good food govern the number of antler points and size of the antlers. A yearling deer on good feed may have three-point antlers and a three-year-old on poor feed may only have one point or spike on each side.

Mule deer may interbreed where the ranges of subspecies meet. Variations in markings and in size may be noted in some deer where there is an overlap in ranges.

The breeding season varies with the elevation and latitude and occurs from October along the coast to November and December in the inland areas. It is generally timed so that the fawns are born at a time when green leafy plants will be available for the young deer. The doe carries the young fawn for about seven months. The peak of the fawning season varies throughout the state, from early April in parts of coastal California to the end of July in places in the Sierra Nevada. Fawns are born with spotted coats but lose their spots at about the time they are weaned. Fawns are usually weaned from 60 to 90 days after birth, but they continue to run with their mothers till fall.

For its first few weeks the fawn is trusting and helpless. When danger threatens, a warning bleat from the mother signals it to hide, while she runs away to distract the intruder. Many times the baby just sinks to the ground and lies still, depending on its protective coloring to keep it from being seen. A young fawn is easy to approach, and, because the mother isn't seen, people assume the baby is lost and they want to take the baby home and care for it. All the while the mother is anxiously watching from nearby cover. The fawns as babies are adorable, but they soon grow up and become a nuisance and later even become dangerous. There are numerous reports of "pet" deer injuring and even killing people. Laws have been passed to prevent people from "adopting" babies of the wild. It is illegal to have a fawn in your possession.

Early California records show that in pioneer times deer were plentiful in the valleys and foothills. After the gold rush deer populations commenced to decline. The settlers' use of meat and hides of wild game was unrestricted. Free grazing on public lands caused a buildup of livestock that resulted in severe overgrazing of the land. These things coupled with the severe winters at the turn of the century caused the deer population to reach its lowest numbers. But despite the rapid encroachment of civilization deer have made a comeback. Today, deer are the most abundant and most popular big game animal in California.

The increase of deer has been the result of many things, the most important of which is the ability of deer to live close to human beings. Next, the fact that when food is abundant, a deer herd is capable of doubling its numbers each year. Like the sheep, a healthy doe normally has twin fawns. Land use was an important factor in the increase of deer populations. The clearing of foothill and mountain homesteads, the cutting of timber, forest fires, and the general opening up of our forests have allowed and encouraged the spread of herbs and browse-type brush, to actually improve the deer range. The establishment of protective laws gave the adaptable deer enough protection to take advantage of their ability to reproduce, and now California has one of the largest herds in the nation.

Evidence of their abundance is shown by the increase in crop depredation, and the disheartening effects of overgrazing. In many areas the deer are eating up their natural forage faster than it can replenish itself. In areas where this occurs, losses resulting from malnutrition soon follow. The die-off result is a needless waste of both deer and range forage.

Sound deer management requires the annual removal of surplus animals of both sexes to keep the animals in balance with their food supplies and other habitat requirements. Consideration must also be given to other land uses in determining the desirable population level to which the deer herds should be held. If the deer and the land are properly managed there will be enough for everyone to enjoy.

DESERT TORTOISE

WILDLIFE LEAFLET

State of California
DEPARTMENT OF FISH AND GAME

THE FRIENDLY TORTOISE IS MORE AT HOME IN THE DESERT THAN IN YOUR BACKYARD

The desert tortoise is a source of endless curiosity to visitors of California's southeastern deserts. Few persons, young or old, who have stopped to view or examine this patient animal can suppress a feeling of wonderment, when they learn that the tortoise has existed on earth in virtually its present form for millions of years.

The tortoise is a member of the reptile family which is composed of snakes, lizards, crocodiles, and "chelonians" or turtles. The turtles are different than other reptiles and are recognized by the complete absence of teeth, and the shell or bony box, that completely covers their body. The shell is actually a part of their body. Except for the tender young, it protects them from nearly all enemies except man. There are about 250 kinds of chelonians or turtles living in the warm belt around the globe. Like all other reptiles they cannot survive in permanently frozen regions. Authorities state that about one quarter of the turtles live in North America.

Evolution down through time has caused some of the turtles to adapt themselves to salt water, some to fresh water and some to land but they are all bound to land, for their eggs cannot hatch unless they are buried in warm sand or decomposing vegetation.

Most persons in the United States call all chelonians turtles, and speak of the fresh water varieties that are used for food as terrapins. The ones that are strictly land forms, that have the high arched shell and stumpy hind legs, are called tortoises. The adult desert tortoise may be as much as 12 inches long. The carapace or shell is dome shaped and marked with an attractive design caused by growth rings. The tail is short. The legs, particularly the hind legs, are elephantoid, much different than the flipperlike legs of those turtles that adapted to the sea. The overall color ranges from a yellowish brown to a dark brown and blends in with the desert colors making them difficult to see when they are not moving. When a tortoise decides to go somewhere it moves at a stolid pace of about 20 feet

per minute. Desert tortoise males average a little larger than the females. When compared, the male's tail is a little longer than the female's and the bottom of his shell is concave. They have adapted themselves to live in the deserts of the southwest. In California they are found in northeastern Los Angeles, eastern Kern, southeastern Inyo Counties and over most of San Bernardino, Riverside and Imperial Counties.

Like the other cold-blooded reptiles that cannot control their body temperatures, tortoises are sensitive to both heat and cold. Consequently they are most active in summer between the cold mornings and the early heat of the day, or on overcast or rainy days. In October, when daytime temperatures get cold, they enter burrows, which they dig themselves, and hibernate until the following March. In the spring when they first "come out" they take very little food, but as the days get warmer they eat grass and the blossoms and tender parts of plants. Although able to go without food for as much as a year, when food is available they seem to eat as much, proportionately as other animals. They can go without water for months, but here again, they are prodigious drinkers. One medium-sized specimen increased its weight by a little more than 40 percent with one long drink.

Sometime between June and November the female digs a shallow nest and carefully deposits from two to six snow-white eggs. She spends a little over an hour digging and covering her eggs. Hatchings have been observed from August to November. The length of time to hatch may be governed by temperatures.

The young like the old are masters at concealment and it is their only means of defense, for they do not run or attempt to escape when approached. The shells do not harden until they are three years old, and the shell remains flexible till they are five or six years old. Tortoises reach about three-fourths of their growth in six or seven years and continue to grow slowly for at least that many more. There are no records of how long the desert tortoise lives, but turtles live longer than any other vertebrate, including man. It is reported that one lived in captivity for 152 years. It was killed accidentally.

Before laws were passed giving the desert tortoise complete protection, many were picked up to be sold as tourist oddities, or taken home as pets. Away from their desert home, and without proper care, they would escape or perish. So if you visit the desert and are lucky enough to encounter a tortoise, look at it, examine it and leave it there, and remember that all this gentle inoffensive creature asks of man is to be left alone.

ELK

WILDLIFE LEAFLET

State of California
DEPARTMENT OF FISH AND GAME

ELK ONCE ROAMED IN GREAT NUMBERS IN THE SAN JOAQUIN VALLEY

THE ELK, NEXT TO THE MOOSE, is the largest member of the North American deer family.

There are three races of elk now present in California—they are the tule, Roosevelt, and Rocky Mountain.

When the early settlers first came to California they found elk in great numbers in the San Joaquin Valley and in the foothills on either side of the valley. They named them the tule elk.

The tule elk in general size and shape looks like other elk. It is sometimes called the dwarf elk because it is not as large as the Roosevelt elk, which weighs nearly 1,000 pounds. A big bull tule elk may weigh 700 pounds.

The tule elk was originally a valley animal and was found only in California. It did not migrate to the mountains in summer like other elk, although in the rainy winter months it would move into the low foothills on either side of the lush central valley.

The explorers also found a larger elk in California which was named the Roosevelt elk. It lived in, and is still found in, the north coast counties and in Oregon and Washington.

Roosevelt elk are inhabitants of the rain forests and coastal area from Humboldt County northward to Vancouver Island and the mainland of British Columbia. These animals reportedly reach greater size than the Rocky Mountain elk. A large bull may weigh between 1,000 and 1,200 pounds. The Roosevelt elk appears equally at home in the mountains or the lowlands and may or may not be migratory, depending on the climate and severity of weather.

Rocky Mountain elk are between tule and Roosevelt elk in size. The mature bulls will weigh from 600 to 1,000 pounds and the females from 500 to 550.

TULE ELK BULL

Rocky Mountain elk are primarily mountain dwellers. Like the mule deer, these elk ordinarily are migratory, spending the winter concentrated in the foothills or adjacent plains but moving up to scatter widely over the mountains during the summer period. The Rocky Mountain elk was the subspecies of widest distribution on this continent, but is not a native of California. Some individuals were transplanted here into Shasta and Monterey counties.

All races of elk have common characteristics. The males alone, perhaps the most stately of American deer, bear beautiful antlers which in the Rocky Mountain variety have been recorded up to 66 inches along the main beam. The antlers are similar to those of the deer in structure, shedding, and growth, but not in shape. A typical head has six points on each side, but this may be exceeded. By March these antlers are shed and by September are fully grown again, and the bull is in his full glory.

Both bulls and cows have reddish summer coats with darker head and legs. The rump patch has a tawny appearance. In winter the long winter coat appears brown, varying from gray on the sides to very dark head and legs. The tule elk's coat is paler both winter and summer than the other varieties of elk.

In September, as soon as the antlers are fully developed, the mating season occurs. The bull makes his presence known by "bugling" a clear musical whistle that calls the cows to him. Each bull, by his dominance, holds the cows together in a harem band. Cows carry their young about 8½ months; a single calf is born in May or June of the following year.

The calf is spotted when born and is eating green vegetation by the time it is a month old. The calf can take care of itself by fall, but may stay with its mother through the winter.

All subspecies of elk can interbreed. This may account for some mixing in areas where ranges overlap. It is estimated that there are about 3,000 elk living in a wild and free-roaming state in California today.

In early times, the growing towns and increasing populations made a ready market for meat and hides. The great herds of elk which seemed like an inexhaustible source dwindled to such a point that in 1873 a law was passed making the killing of an elk a felony punishable by imprisonment up to two years.

Under complete protection the elk survived. But, as more and more people moved to California and more land was developed, the tule elk was displaced from San Joaquin Valley. A remnant herd of tule elk is maintained in a state park at Tupman, near Bakersfield. A small herd of 75 or 100 known as the Cache Creek herd is still found free-roaming in Colusa County, and a transplant of tule elk to Owens Valley is presently being managed to hold their numbers between 250 and 300. There are approximately 2,000 Roosevelt elk in the north coast counties and about 700 Rocky Mountain elk in Monterey and San Luis Obispo counties and in the Shasta Lake area.

Conflict with agriculture has been the most serious problem connected with maintaining California elk herds. Crop damage, damage to fencing, and overgrazing constitute the main problems. In the case of large animals like elk, it is necessary to control their numbers prudently for the sake of their own health and to avoid serious conflict with other uses of the land. This has proven true in every state where elk damage occurs. The Department of Fish and Game, under the authorization of the Fish and Game Commission, has conducted special elk hunts in some areas in order to control the numbers of animals using the limited range.

Scientists and biologists keep a constant check on the elks' ranges, and, unless our ever-increasing population makes too great a demand on land use, the people will continue to retain and enjoy a limited use of this magnificent animal.

California Wildlife Information Sheet

The Resources Agency of California—Department of Fish and Game

Golden Trout

The golden trout is native only to California and, by an act of the State Legislature in 1947, was named the official State Fish. This was an appropriate choice, for the golden is the most beautiful of all trouts. Brightly colored, it has a medium dark-olive back, shading down through lighter olive and lemon-golden sides to a brilliant orange to cherry-red belly. There are reddish-orange stripes midway along the sides from head to tail, broken by dull-olive vertical bars called parr marks. On some, the head, back, tail, and dark-olive back fins are marked with clear black dots. The other fins are bright orange, usually tipped with white. These bright colors become almost gaudy at spawning time.

The golden trout was first described by fisheries scientists over 70 years ago. Originally it only occurred in a few of the streams in the upper reaches of the Kern River drainage in Tulare County. Stocking of wild and hatchery-reared fish has extended its range to many waters at high elevation in the Sierra Nevada from El Dorado and Alpine Counties southward. It has also been planted in other states. Recent plants in Trinity and Siskiyou Counties are being watched with interest by fisheries scientists. These waters will remain closed to fishing until it is determined if they are successful.

The golden trout thrives in California waters at elevations from 8,500 to 10,500 feet. It has been found as low as 6,300 feet. In most streams it remains small, from 5 to 8 inches. In some lakes it may grow much larger, 12 to 18 inches. The largest golden trout reported from California weighed 9 pounds 14 ounces. The world's record weighed 11 pounds. It was caught in Wyoming.

The goldens, like the native rainbow trout, spawn in the spring. In the high alpine life zone in which the golden thrive, spring as we know it comes in June and July. When air temperatures warm up, the ice disappears, and the deep snows melt away. When water temperatures reach a certain degree, a mysterious urge sends the restless trout in search of a gravel bar in which to build their nests and lay their eggs. In streams that have a constant flow the goldens spawn successfully, and have been able to maintain their numbers, despite the gradual increase in fishing pressures.

Unlike lake and eastern brook trout, the goldens don't spawn in the quiet lake waters. Many of the rockbound lakes in which goldens have been planted do not have tributary streams that are suitable for spawning. These lakes need to be periodically replanted with hatchery-reared fish.

Rainbows and golden trout interbreed. In lakes where they have been planted together, variations occur and sometimes there has been a complete loss of color. Fisheries scientists, conservationists and sportsmen are all keenly interested in maintaining a pure strain of golden trout. One small lake which contains a pure strain of goldens has been set aside as a brood pond. Here and in other waters where a pure strain of goldens exists, crews of men spawn these fish artificially. The eggs are then taken to a fish hatchery where they are

THE GOLDEN TROUT

hatched separately. When the baby fish are about two inches long they are in turn planted in suitable waters. In years past this was done with pack stock and sometimes men laboriously carried them in with backpacks. Now an airplane is used and the fingerlings are dropped into the lakes from the air. The department may plant some lakes in which eastern brook trout are established, for the eastern brook and golden do not interbreed. But for the most part goldens are either planted in waters that contain no other trout or waters that are already planted with golden trout.

Men feel differently about fishing for golden trout than they do about regular trout fishing. One reason is that golden trout waters are not accessible by roads. To seek the golden trout one must hike far back into the primitive high country. This places a natural restriction on the numbers of persons who fish for goldens. In this remote country the golden is easily caught. The short summers limit the natural food supply so goldens take artificial flies, lures and baits readily. The small lakes, crystal-clear mountain meadow streams, and hungry fish makes the golden vulnerable to overfishing. However, many people find the beauty and grandeur of the surroundings so satisfying there is no urge to fish for "limits." A few of these beautiful trout caught to examine, to admire and to eat in camp seems enough in itself.

So far the remoteness of the areas in which goldens are found, and the lack of roads, have kept it possible to maintain this unique trout. As long as a part of the magnificent area in which the golden originated is allowed to remain isolated from motor vehicles, those who are willing to take the time and effort may hike into this wild and rugged "high country" and still find the spectacular golden trout.

FLY FISHING IN GOLDEN TROUT COUNTRY

JACKRABBIT

WILDLIFE LEAFLET

State of California
DEPARTMENT OF FISH AND GAME

Jackrabbits are true hares. The hares, unlike the cottontailed rabbits, do not build a nest. The mother just chooses a place to her liking and the young are born, fully furred, with their eyes wide open. They are able to hop around soon after they are born.

There are three members of the hare family native to California: the blacktail, the whitetail, and the snowshoe or varying hare. The black-tailed and white-tailed hares are commonly called jackrabbits. The snowshoe or varying hare is known as the snowshoe rabbit.

The white-tailed jack is the largest of California's hare family. It weighs from six to eight pounds. In winter, it is sometimes mistaken for the snowshoe rabbit, for, in the colder parts of its range, individuals turn completely white. The range of the white-tailed jack in California is restricted to the east side of the Sierra and Cascade Mountains from Tulare County north to the Oregon border. Unlike the black-tailed jack, which prefers to live in the flat open country and in the valley, the white-tailed jack lives in the hills and mountains. In their summer coat, in areas where the ranges of these two jackrabbits overlaps, there may be some confusion as to identity. However the two may be distinguished by the color of the underside of their tails. The tail of the black-tailed jack is brownish underneath; the tail of the white-tailed jack is white.

The snowshoe or varying hare is more easily identified. It is the smallest hare. It looks more like a cottontail rabbit. Its ears are shorter than its head, but the underside of its tail is brown, not white like the cottontail. The snowshoe rabbit, like the white-tailed jack, also goes through two annual molts. In early winter it turns snow white, except for the tips of its ears, which remain black. Its feet become covered with a mat of long hair, to help it run over the soft snow, thus its name "snowshoe". In late spring it molts again to a summer coat of grayish brown. The snowshoe rabbit's range is a long narrow strip from the Oregon border down through the higher elevations of the Klamath, Cascade, and Sierra Mountains as far south as Tuolumne County. There are a few snowshoe rab-

bits in the Warner Mountains in Modoc County. The snowshoe is seldom seen for it prefers to live in dense fir thickets and in winter is isolated by deep snow.

The snowshoe rabbit and the white-tailed jack may have more than one litter a year. There can be as many as seven or eight in a litter, although the average litter is from two to four.

The black-tailed jack is by far the most common and is found all over California except in the mountainous areas at elevations above 12,000 feet. They adapt themselves readily to man's use of the land and thrive even in highly developed areas.

In the more temporate areas of the black-tailed jack's range, breeding may continue the year around. Usually several litters are born each year. Here again there may be as many as eight but the average litter is from two to four. The mother hides her young when she goes out to feed, and, upon returning, mother and young call to locate each other.

The hares have many natural enemies. Coyotes, bobcats, foxes, horned owls, hawks and snakes prey on both the young and adults. At higher elevations the marten and fisher also prey on the snowshoe.

The hares are mostly active at night. During the day they lie crouched in a "form" which they have made by using the same spot in a clump of grass or weeds. With their long ears flattened against their back they are difficult to see. Frequently on hot summer days they can be seen resting in the shade of a small bush or even a fencepost. When frightened they run with such speed that few dogs can catch them. At the start of the chase their speed is broken by high long leaps.

The hares are strict vegetarians, eating a great variety of herbs and shrubs. In agricultural areas the black-tailed jack may become a serious pest in young orchards and other agricultural crops.

It is estimated that nearly two million "jackrabbits" are taken by hunters annually in California. The flesh is excellent eating. In periods of high population, some black-tailed jacks, like other game and nongame species may become diseased and carry tularemia or be a host to common animal parasites. While this is of minor consequence to humans, care should be used in handling or skinning all animals, as some diseases are transmissible through open cuts or abrasions. Cooking thoroughly eliminates any danger.

A hunting license is required to hunt all rabbits. There is a season and bag limit on snowshoe rabbits. They are not numerous, and cause no conflict with agriculture. There is no closed season or bag limit on either the white-tailed or black-tailed jackrabbit at present, for they have adapted to our changing environment and are able to withstand constant pursuit by natural predators, both man and beast.

California Wildlife Information Sheet

The Resources Agency of California—Department of Fish and Game

Mountain Lion

The mountain lion, which is sometimes known as cougar, puma, or panther, is the largest member of the cat family now in California. Exceedingly rare, or entirely absent in many eastern states, it is still common in California. Although not normally dangerous to man, the fanciful tales that have been passed along about this big cat make camping out additionally exciting to the seasoned woodsman as well as the tenderfoot.

There are two subspecies of the mountain lion in California. The Yuma mountain lion, which lives in the southeastern deserts of California, and the California mountain lion, which lives in the mountains and brushland all over the State, except in the extreme northeast section and in the Coast Range just north of San Francisco Bay, where it is rare.

The mountain lion appears in two colors. The Yuma race is pale yellow in appearance while the California mountain lion is gray. Both are about the same size, measuring from 6 to 8 feet in length, from nose to tip of tail. The females seldom weigh over 110 pounds, while the males can weigh as much as 165 pounds.

The big cats range over an area about 20 miles wide. The males use a larger area than the females and make regular trips over their range. The female uses a smaller area because she may have young or be teaching last year's cubs the things young lions need to know.

Mountain lions may breed at any time of the year. Most of the young are born during the early summer months. The gestation period is 91 to 97 days, so the peak of the mating season is probably from January to May. Professional lion hunters take advantage of this period, for at this time several females may follow a male on his regular circuit. The young, like house cats, are born with their eyes closed. They are about one foot long when first born and weigh one pound. The cubs are spotted with black markings, which gradually disappear by the time they are a year old. One female lion produced young every second year over an eight-year period, for a total of nine kittens. The kittens stay with the mother until they are over one year old. By this time they weigh about 50 pounds and are becoming skilled enough to stalk and kill small animals and birds for a part of their own food.

Photo by Wyoming Game and Fish Department

Mountain Lion

MOUNTAIN LION PORTRAIT

Photo by New Mexico Department of Game and Fish

Mountain lions rarely scream. They do, however, make a call that is almost a bird-like whistle. People rarely associate this sound with a cat. Its mew is like a house cat's except much louder. The animal also spits explosively and its growl is deep and menacing.

The mountain lions live in the same range as deer. Although they are known to prey on almost any animal found in their range, their principal food item is deer. The big cats usually stalk their prey to within a short distance and then capture in a sudden bounding attack. They kill large animals by biting near the base of the skull. They usually attempt to cover the remains of a kill and return to feed once more.

In 1907 a law was passed requiring the Department of Fish and Game to pay a bounty on mountain lions. This continued until 1963. During this time nearly 13,000 lions were taken. In spite of this number removed, the mountain lion population has remained stable.

The idea of predator control has changed over the years. Today it is felt that mountain lions don't harm wildlife populations. In some areas, where all natural predators like mountain lions have been removed and no hunting is allowed, the game animals like deer have increased to such an extent that they have actually eaten up and destroyed their own source of food. But a stable population of predators can help keep game animal populations in balance with their habitat. Where mountain lions are in direct conflict with livestock the big cats are still killed by federal trappers.

In recent years there has been an increasing number of sportsmen who hunt mountain lions as trophy big game animals.

Elusive in the wild, and shy of man, the big cats are seldom seen; but almost everyone senses the thrill of unknown danger when the big unmistakable tracks of a mountain lion are seen in the dust of some backwoods trail.

MOURNING DOVE

The mourning dove is the most popular upland game bird in California. Actually, there are four kinds of doves found in the state: the mourning dove, white-winged dove, ring-necked dove, and chinese spotted dove.

The ring-necked and chinese doves were imported from the Orient as early as 1921, escaped into the wild in the Los Angeles area, and have spread out into the surrounding suburban areas.

The white-winged dove is native to southeastern California and is found in the Imperial Valley and along the Colorado River. The mourning dove is the most numerous and is found in every state in the United States and in every county in California. The only place it is not common is in the dense evergreen forests and in alpine areas at high elevations.

The mourning dove looks like a sleek pigeon, only a little smaller. The color of the male is a delicately beautiful soft bluish gray, with buff underparts. The sides of the neck gleam lightly with coppery iridescence. The bill is black and the legs and feet are pale red. The female looks like the male except the colors are somewhat duller.

The dove is not a dense forest or marsh bird, but rather prefers farm and orchard lands. It is equally at home in open woodlands and in arid semidesert-type areas.

The dove feeds primarily on weed seeds and uses some cereal grains. Less than 1 percent of its diet is made up of insects.

The male dove selects the nesting place. The female is attracted there by the male's cooing. Doves are easily pleased when it comes to nesting sites. They nest in trees and shrubs, on the ground and even in old buildings. They are not very careful in their nest building, consequently some eggs and young are easily dislodged from the flimsy nest and lost. However, doves renest from two to five times throughout the year. The long breeding period allows them to raise five or six young annually.

The dove normally lays two pure white eggs. Both the male and female sit on the nest to hatch the eggs and help care for the young. The eggs are hatched in 14 days, and the young are cared for in the nest for from 10 to 15 days. Within a week after the youngsters leave the nest the parents ignore them and begin with another clutch of eggs. The male dove's cooing, is of course an indication of nesting activity, and the cooing is followed by a nuptial flight. The male flies up in a steep climb for several hundred feet, sets his wings and sails back on rigid wings, to the nest, in a sweeping arc.

The dove is a migratory bird. Peak populations occur in the northern parts of the state in August, and as cooler weather commences the birds start their southern migration. Banding studies have revealed that some California doves travel far south to a favorite wintering grounds near Jalisco in central Mexico.

The dove, like other migratory birds that move from one state to another, is protected by federal law, and within the framework of federal regulations the state sets rules and regulations to protect the dove from overshooting. Out of a total population of some 20 million birds each year, about 4½ million are taken by California hunters. Under our present regulations the dove population remains stable in California and offers pleasure to both the hunter and the bird lover. Careful management will allow us all to continue to enjoy this beautiful game bird.

California Wildlife Information Sheet

The Resources Agency of California—Department of Fish and Game

Muskrat

The muskrat is a small, plump rodent a little larger than a cottontail rabbit. It is easily identified because it is the only rodent that has a hairless, vertically flattened tail. Its head is small and the little beady eyes and small ears are nearly hidden by its dense, soft fur. Its hind feet are webbed, with fringes of short, stiff hairs. Its webbed feet and the rudder-like tail are indications of its semiaquatic existence. Its fur is cinnamon brown in color and the sides and back are covered with dark glossy guard hairs.

The muskrat gets its name from the two musk glands that lie on its lower belly. During the mating season, the glands secrete a sweet, cloying odor to attract muskrats of the opposite sex. In early times, before toiletries were easily available, young ladies obtained a delicate perfume by placing kerchiefs over unskinned muskrats for sufficient time for them to absorb the fragrance in suitable strength.

Farmers dependent on water for irrigation and owners of ponds dislike the muskrat because of its habit of burrowing in the levees and in the banks of ditches and ponds. Farm boys and trappers like the muskrat because it is easy to trap, easy to skin, and is in constant demand by the fur trade.

The muskrat is semiaquatic and needs water in which to live. Its home is in burrows which it digs in banks along the water's edge. It prefers the main entrance to its home to be under water, and it nearly always provides an exit for escape. In the shallow, marshy waters, it sometimes builds a home of tules, twigs, and mud, which it mounds up above the water line.

The muskrat is nocturnal but occasionally it feeds in daylight hours. Its diet is essentially vegetarian, made up of roots, bulbs, and grasses, although it eats a few mussels and occasionally a frog or a crayfish.

In central California, the mating season is from March to September and all year long in the Colorado River. It has from two to three litters a year with an average of four to the litter. At the age of one month the kits are able to shift for themselves. There are still many kits, too small to be of value, in the composition of the November population of muskrats. They mature rapidly, so the wise trapper

waits till December, when most muskrats are full grown, to commence trapping.

The muskrat is native to the drainage east of the Sierra from Modoc County south to Mono County. A subspecies somewhat smaller and more pale in color, and known in the fur trade as "sand rat," is native to the Colorado River.

Eastern species of the muskrat were introduced into northern California in the late 1920's for fur farming purposes. Some escaped and others were deliberately planted in the Klamath and Pit Rivers.

A muskrat fur farm in Butte County was washed out by a flood in 1938. The muskrats that escaped made their way into the Feather River, and in a few short years had extended their range down the Sacramento and up the San Joaquin Rivers and now they are found in most of the waters in the great valley.

The muskrat fur is soft, thick and durable and can be used in so many ways that it has become the "backbone" of the fur trade.

Nearly 20,000,000 skins are used annually in the United States.

In California, the muskrat has increased to a point where it is now the most important fur taken in California, by volume of numbers caught and by cash value. The estimated catch is 100,000 annually, with a cash value to the trapper of $80,000.

The muskrat population has not reached the saturation point and will continue to spread with the increase in water distribution for irrigation. In intensively irrigated farmlands in central California, the muskrat is considered a nuisance, due to its habit of burrowing, and is not protected by fish and game laws. In northern California, it is protected as a furbearer and can be taken only during the fur trapping season. (See current hunting regulations.)

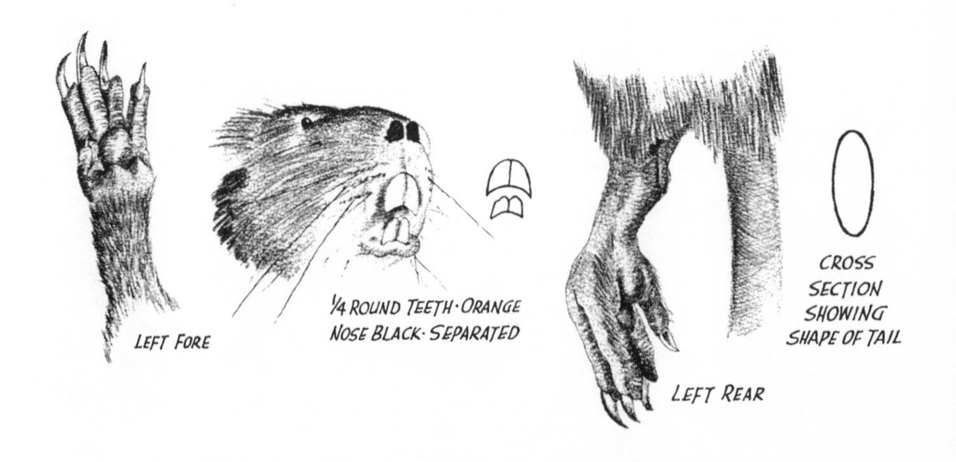

The Resources Agency–Department of Fish and Game

PHEASANT

THIS FOREIGN IMPORT IS NOW CALIFORNIA'S MOST SPECTACULAR GAME BIRD

The pheasant is the most spectacular upland game bird in California. It is native to China and other parts of eastern Asia. In 1889 the Department of Fish and Game (then the State Board of Fish and Game Commissioners) introduced several varieties of pheasant into California. The Chinese ringneck pheasant is the only species that was successful in establishing breeding populations. The first hunting season was in 1925 in Owens Valley. The first statewide season was in 1933 and has been in effect since then. The Chinese ringneck is a gaudily colored bird with distinctive brilliant plumage, a white ring around his neck, and, when fully matured, a black banded tail that may be as much as 21 inches in length. The female is smaller and also has a long pointed tail. She is quite drab by contrast. Her coloring could be described as a mottled blend of grays and browns with some buff and dusky markings.

During the winter pheasants tend to separate into bands of hens and bands of cocks. In February and March the cocks spread out to look for a territory of their own. These home areas are defined by crowing and display, and are defended by much bluffing and even fighting. The size of the home areas varies from 3 to 13 acres according to the density of the cover and the availability of food and water.

In late March and early April the hens gradually disperse and join the roosters in the crowing grounds for harem formation, which is usually from three to five hens per rooster.

The hen builds her nest in grassy or weedy places. She lays from 10 to 12 pale olive-colored eggs which are hatched in from 23 to 25 days. The young are ready to leave the nest when they are dry. Both the father and mother are good parents. The father guards the young of all the hens in his harem and although he is not with any one of his families, he responds immediately at the first note of alarm.

The baby pheasants' food the first week is made up almost entirely of insects, but by the time they are 12 weeks old they eat the same diet as their parents, which is made up of cereal grains, wild weed seeds, the green leaves of plants, and some insects.

Young pheasant broods are seclusive and are difficult to flush. Although they can fly when three weeks old they prefer to run when danger threatens, even after they are grown. In August the young show some independence, and by late September the fully feathered birds from different territories join each other in areas that have the most suitable protective cover.

The flight of an adult pheasant is strong. When cornered at the edge of cover, or by a hunting dog, it bursts from the ground, sometimes with a raucous cackling cry that unnerves the hunter. The wing action is rapid and the speed of flight may reach 35 miles per hour. The flights are usually low, 10 or 15 feet from the ground, and when shot at pheasants may fly and coast on stiff set wings for 200 yards or more.

Ringnecked pheasants have been introduced into every county in California, but satisfactory breeding populations became established only in the fertile valley areas of diversified agriculture, where there is a plentiful year-round supply of water and some grain farming.

The largest populations are found in the rice-growing areas in Sacramento and upper San Joaquin Valleys, and in the Tule Lake area. The most important of these is the rice-growing area of the Sacramento Valley. The abundant water needs for rice culture promotes heavy growths of cover along the many canals, ditches, sloughs and low spots suitable for high pheasant populations.

Most of the land in the valleys of California is private property, and permission is required from landowners to hunt on their property. Due to the tremendous increase in human population since World War II and due also to the intensification of land use, there has been a trend among landowners to control and limit hunting. Competition for areas to hunt has become keen, and the wise sportsman must plan well in advance of the hunting seasons, if he wishes to have a spot to hunt the wily ringneck.

Ringneck pheasants. Photo by U.S. Fish and Wildlife Service.

PILEATED WOODPECKER

State of California
DEPARTMENT OF FISH AND GAME

THIS NOISY FOREST RESIDENT IS ONE OF OUR LARGEST BIRDS

Except for the ivory-billed, the pileated woodpecker is the largest member of this colorful family of North American birds. The male is nearly as large as a crow. He is 18 inches long and has a wingspread of 28 inches. The male is slightly larger than the female.

Unlike all other woodpeckers, both the male and female wear a pointed cap or crest on the crown of their head, hence the name pileated. The entire crown and crest is a bright poppy red and was prized by the Indians in early days for feather decorations.

The male and female are similar in color. The body is a dull black with contrasting stripes of white on the neck and white underparts on the wings. The large size and flashing black and white color, coupled with their strident cry, make them easy to identify in flight, even at a long distance. They have a variety of notes, the most common is whĭ, whĭ, whĭ, which is made in flight. When two or more are together you hear a conversation of low notes with an occasional kyuck----kyuck, kyuck. After you have learned some of these notes, because they are so far reaching in the quiet of the forest, you become aware that this big woodpecker is more common than supposed.

The pileated woodpecker is widely distributed throughout the heavily wooded portions of North America. It is known locally by different names such as log cock, black wood cock, cock of the woods, and others. Its gradual disappearance from some eastern areas and from parts of its former range in California is associated with the extension of the lumbering operations, for it is rarely seen in cut-over areas.

In California it is still found from Oregon south, down the coastal mountains to Sonoma County and from Mt. Shasta-Lassen area south in the Sierra to the Greenhorn Mountains in Tulare County.

It prefers to live and nest in the dense original growths of fir and aspen, although it has been observed at lower elevations along the coast. It thrives best where there are old, dead trees both standing and rotting on the ground, for these are the source of the ants, beetles, and grubs that make up most of its food.

The big woodpecker has a bill longer than its head and is so powerful that it can peck, rend, and tear its way through the thick bark of an old fir tree to find the beetles and grubs that live under the bark. Even more interesting is its long, barbed tongue. It can stick its tongue out four or five inches past the end of its bill. It uses its tongue to probe in the tunnels of wood-boring ants and grubs and fishes them out with a quick flicking motion. Rotten logs are a favorite feeding place. A pair of "log cocks" in their search for bugs can literally tear a log to bits in one season.

When hiking through dense uncut groves of trees, look for the telltale signs that indicate a pileated woodpecker's presence. These are trees and tall stumps. They may also be an indicator of a nest, which could be 40 or 50 feet up in an aspen or fir tree. If the entrance to a nest is found, strike the base of the tree and you may be rewarded by seeing one leave the nest.

The male and female both work for nearly a month to chisel out a suitable nest. The entrance hole is from three to four inches across. The nest cavity is 18 inches deep and five to six inches wide at the bottom.

A covering of soft wood chips is left on the bottom for the nest. The female starts to lay her eggs in early May. She lays from three to six snow-white eggs. They are so smooth they look like porcelain. It takes the eggs 18 days to hatch. The young are hatched naked and blind, but both parents seem very happy to take care of their young and take turns feeding, brooding, and caring for them. The young remain on or near the nest tree for several days after they leave the nest. Then they follow the parents for many weeks. They are noisy and busy learning when and how to find the

Photo courtesy Maine Fish and Game

choicest bugs. Parent birds may nest in the same area year after year.

Since there is no conflict with man, the big, black cock of the woods should remain in our mountains for many years to come, at least in numbers that are commensurate with the groves of uncut forest that are left. It should remain to continue its role in the ecology of the forest, and to thrill the occasional wilderness hiker with its colorful presence or tantalize him with its derisive, laughterlike call as it flies steadily ahead—nearly always just out of sight.

California Wildlife Information Sheet

The Resources Agency of California—Department of Fish and Game

Pronghorn Antelope

The pronghorn, commonly called antelope, is not a true antelope but is in a family all by itself. It is placed there mainly on account of its horns. This species is the only antelope like form that has branched horns. It is strictly a North American mammal and does not occur naturally in any other country in the world.

The horns are true horns which grow over a bony core, like cattle, sheep, goats and true antelopes. Unlike that group, which keeps the same horns through life, the pronghorn sheds the outside shell each year. The horns of the female are much smaller than the males. The bucks' horns have been recorded at over 20 inches in length.

The pronghorn is about the size of a blacktail deer. The does average about 90 pounds while the bucks average about 112 pounds. Unlike the deer, they don't attempt to hide in heavy brush or timber but prefer to live in open, grassy and sagebrush plains where they can see long distances. They depend on their exceptionally keen eyesight and speed to escape from their enemies. Their eyes protrude like a rabbit's and are placed so they can see in all directions. The pronghorn appears awkward when walking, but is most graceful when running at top speed. They seem to enjoy running and will race along beside a car, suddenly speed ahead, and cross over in front of the car almost as though to prove their speed. They have been clocked at 60 miles per hour, the swiftest mammal in the Western Hemisphere.

To provide added protection, nature gave the pronghorn a bright coat of reddish tan, marked with white and black. Close by it appears colorful, however, the peculiar markings tend to break up the outline of the body so well that at a distance, they are difficult to recognize while lying down or standing still. The long white hair on their rump can be raised at will. When alarmed a band of pronghorns will face the intruder and rapidly raise or spread the snow-white hairs on their rump as a warning signal to other distant bands of their own kind.

In summer they eat some grasses and leafy plants like sheep. In winter sagebrush is the main source of food. They move in bands from summer range to winter range where the snow is not so deep.

Pronghorn Group — Wyoming Game and Fish Photo

The breeding season is in September. The mother carries the young 240 days before giving birth. A young doe usually has only one kid. After that twins are common. The kids are not spotted like fawn deer, but are grayish brown so they can hide in the grass and sagebrush. By the time they are three weeks old they can run tirelessly with the band. They grow rapidly and by fall they can take care of themselves and it is then hard to tell them from adults.

In the early days of California the pronghorn was found in great numbers all through the central and southern valleys and deserts in California. The rapid development of the State and the unrestricted killing by the early settlers, soon reduced their numbers and now they are only found in the northeastern part of the state. The increase in the use of sheeptight fencing has also restricted the pronghorn's range. Although pronghorn can jump 20 feet in distance, if they can't go through a fence or under it, a sheep-tight fence will stop them.

The area in which they prefer to live is used by sheep, cattle and deer. This limits the numbers of pronghorn that can live there.

Pronghorn are readily observed from the air so it is easy for game managers to keep a close check on their numbers. When it is determined the herd has increased to a point greater than the limited amount of range that is suitable for them, the Department of Fish and Game may request a special hunt to control their numbers. Hunters consider the pronghorn a trophy animal and look forward eagerly to an opportunity to bag one of California's most interesting kinds of big game.

Montana Fish and Game Photo

Pronghorn Antelope

California Wildlife Information Sheet

The Resources Agency of California—Department of Fish and Game

Quail

GAMBEL QUAIL—UNLIKE THE VALLEY QUAIL, THE MALE HAS A RUST-RED CAP

MALE AND FEMALE VALLEY QUAIL

The California valley quail is our official State Bird. It was adopted by the State Legislature in 1931. It is also one of the most popular upland game birds in the State. Nearly one-third of the licensed hunters find all or part of their sport in pursuit of quail.

Almost everyone enjoys watching a covey of quail and listening to the clear distinct notes of their call.

There are two other kinds of quail in California, the mountain quail and the desert or gambel quail. These are not as widespread in California as the valley quail.

MT. QUAIL (SEXES ALIKE)

Distribution

The valley quail is found almost everywhere in California except in the high mountains and desert areas in southeastern California.

The mountain quail is found in the high mountains from the Mexico border to Oregon in both the Coast and Sierra Nevada ranges and in the high desert ranges of Southern California. In winter in areas where it snows the mountain quail migrates to lower elevations. As soon as the snows melt, it returns to the higher elevations.

The Gambel or desert quail is found in the deserts of southeastern California and along the Colorado River.

Life History

Quail belong to the chickenlike birds. They spend most of their time on the ground scratching for food. At night they perch in bushes or trees where they are safe from their enemies. During the fall and winter months they live in coveys of from 6 birds to 60 or more.

In early spring the coveys break up. The quail then go in pairs. They nest on the ground, and both the female and male help in nest building. The male chooses only one mate for the season. The female lays from 10 to 15 creamy white eggs that are lightly spotted with golden brown. The

VALLEY QUAIL FAMILY

VALLEY QUAIL

GAMBEL QUAIL

eggs must be kept warm for 22 days before they hatch, so the female and sometimes the male sets them day and night.

Almost as soon as the chicks break out of the shell and become dry they are ready to leave the nest. Young quail are hard to find because they are the same color as dried grass. In the spring they eat green vegetation, seeds, and insects; and in late summer, fall, and winter they eat mostly berries, seeds, and small insects.

Management

In the early days of California, quail were more numerous than today. Changes in agricultural practices, including overgrazing, have destroyed the homes where quail once lived. This has reduced quail populations in many areas.

The Department of Fish and Game has found the quail to be rather easily managed. Quail need three things: food, water, and cover in which to escape from enemies.

The Department of Fish and Game investigates locations to find out what is needed to create the proper quail habitat. Programs can then be planned or recommended to manage the land so that quail will thrive. This is done by supplying water in dry desert areas, and also by planting grasses and shrubs for roosting and escape cover. Under our present laws and practice, suitable areas throughout California have stable and healthy quail populations.

MOUNTAIN QUAIL

SAGE GROUSE

The sage grouse or sagehen, as it is commonly called, is the largest member of North America's grouse family. The adult males are nearly twice as large as the hens. They are almost as large as a hen turkey. Both the male and female are similar in appearance. They are strikingly marked with gray, buff, brown, and black. The underparts are white, and a large black belly patch distinguishes them from other grouse. Both have long, sharp-pointed tails.

The colors blend so well with the soft grays and brown of the sagebrush that it is startling when a flock of these big birds burst into flight. The wing beat is heavy, but they gather speed rapidly, and sometimes fly for as much as a mile with an alternating series of flappings and gently rising and falling glides on stiff set wings.

In late winter and spring all the male birds from an area of several square miles gather at dawn on habitually used strutting grounds and perform one of the most unusual and spectacular courtship displays of all game birds. The full season of activity may extend up to two or three months ending usually in May.

The male starts to strut by arching the spiked tail in full spread. The patches of white feathers on each side of the breast are raised to frame his proud black head. Turning this way and that, he partially inflates the air sacs on his neck. The wings droop stiffly and he inhales air in gulps to complete the inflation of the sacs, and then runs forward with mincing steps. The wings scrape with a swishing noise. This action is repeated several times, the whole air sac region bounces, and the sacs' deflation is accompanied by a plopping sound. This may occur 10 or 15 times a minute as he shows off to attract a mate. This display, if undisturbed, may continue from dawn for as much as two hours. The females visit the spot daily toward the end of the strutting period.

The female makes a shallow nest under a sagebush. She lays from seven to eight grayish or greenish drab colored eggs dotted rather thickly with reddish brown. The eggs hatch in 25 days and the young are ready to

leave the nest when the last one hatched is dry.

The hen takes complete care of the nest and chicks, teaching them feeding habits and how to escape danger when she calls a warning. If she can't distract the danger by pretending injury she will sometimes attack by flying at the enemy with loud cackling and hissing noises.

The young birds eat insects but quickly commence the diet of the older birds. The sage grouse does not have a gizzard but takes the food directly into its stomach. The older birds eat insects and green plants and grasses in spring and early summer, but in fall and winter they eat only the leaves of the big sage. This specialized diet confines the sage grouse exclusively to the Great Basin sagebrush-type country.

In California the sage grouse is found only in the northeastern counties and down the easterly side of the Sierra Nevada to northern Inyo County. Lassen and Mono Counties have the most stable populations. They are found in greatest abundance where there is a combination of sagebrush, grassy meadows, and water.

Experienced hunters try for the younger birds in the flock because the adults have a strong sage flavor. It is advisable to clean and cool the birds immediately after they are killed. If properly handled, young birds have a delicious flavor and can be prepared like domestic chicken.

Because of their limited range and numbers in California the sage grouse is considered a minor game species. The isolated areas in which they live, coupled with a short season and small bag limit, causes a natural restriction on their pursuit, but for the person who loves the sagebrush country and is willing to walk long distances, the sage grouse is an exciting and unusual game bird.

California Wildlife Information Sheet

The Resources Agency of California—Department of Fish and Game

Spotted Skunk

Skunks

There are two kinds of skunks in California, the striped skunk and the spotted skunk. They are similar in many ways; both have glossy coats of black, marked with white in stripes and spots which gave them their names.

The striped skunk is about the size of a plump housecat. The spotted skunk is smaller; about as big as a half-grown cat. Both of these skunks belong to the weasel family.

Skunks are not very good fighters or runners but they possess a potent secret weapon—a strong-smelling scent gland at the base of their tail. When cornered or molested they stamp their front feet in warning and turn so the gland opening is aimed at the intruder. The little spotted skunk may become so excited that it will whirl around and stand up on its front feet. This may look cute, but duck, he's just taking better aim. If they are attacked the powerful oily scent can be ejected in a spray for about 10 feet. If left alone they will turn and scamper away.

The skunks eat a variety of food. In spring and summer they eat fruits, berries, eggs, all kinds of insects, small rodents and reptiles. In winter they dig insects and small rodents out of the ground. Their digging leaves little cone-shaped holes.

They usually live in underground burrows which they may dig if the ground is soft. Otherwise they use the vacant homes of other small animals, hollow logs and rockpiles. They also like to live in old haystacks and in the space under old buildings. Both skunks are nocturnal and are seldom seen in daylight hours.

The skunks do not hibernate, although they do sometimes group together in one den and sleep through short periods of the coldest weather.

The mating season is in February and March, and the young are born in 63 days. The striped skunk has from 4 to 10 babies in a litter. The spotted skunk rarely has more than 6. Although skunks are born blind and helpless, like kittens, they develop rapidly and are out hunting with their mother in six weeks.

Skunks are distributed widely in California. They adapt themselves to a variety of surroundings. The striped skunk thrives in low mountains,

Striped Skunk Youngsters

Striped Skunk

valley farmlands and even among suburban dwellers. It never strays far from water and seems to favor old ditches and stream banks where the brush is dense. The spotted skunk does not confine itself so closely to water and prefers the rocky, brushy hillsides more than the open floor of the valley.

During the late 1920's the shiny black fur of the striped skunk was very popular and trappers caught them for the fur markets. In 1927 trappers reported catching 56,000 skunks. At that time they were worth as much as $5 each, and trapping controlled their numbers to a certain extent. In 1963 trappers reported catching less than 400 skunks.

A skunk skin is now worth less than one dollar, so trappers do not bother to catch them. Because of this, and the increased distribution of water because of agriculture, skunks are more plentiful.

Because of their nocturnal habits and shy nature, skunks are very little bother to people. Occasionally—like other uncontrolled wild animals—skunk numbers build up in restricted locations, and overcrowding can cause disease outbreaks. This can be a nuisance, particularly in suburban areas.

But for the most part skunks are very good animals to have around, because they eat so many destructive insects and small rodents.

"Spotted Skunk on the Defensive"

California Wildlife Information Sheet

The Resources Agency of California—Department of Fish and Game

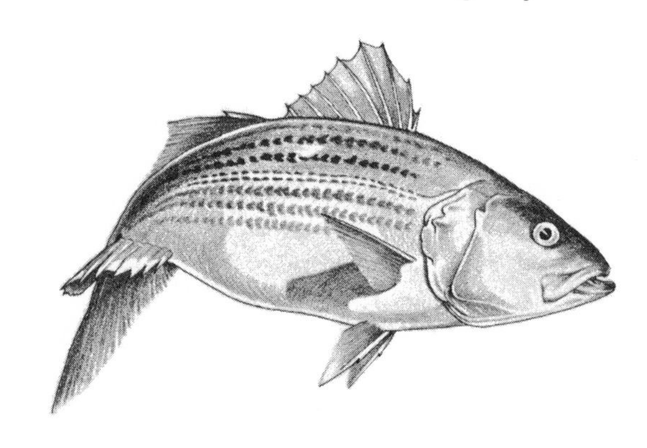

Striped Bass

The striped bass has long been one of California's top-ranking sport fish. Originally there were no striped bass in California. They were introduced from the east coast, where they are found from the Gulf of St. Lawrence to Florida. The first introduction into California was made in 1879 when 132 small bass were brought by rail from New Jersey and released near Martinez. In 1882 a second planting of about 300 young fish was made in lower Suisun Bay.

Before many years striped bass were being caught in California in large numbers. Ten years after the first release, stripers were being sold in San Francisco markets, and in another 10 years the catch by commercial netters was averaging over 1,000,000 pounds a year. Interest in sport fishing increased to the point where in 1935 all commercial netting of stripers was stopped by law and since then only anglers have been permitted to fish for them.

Striped bass are beautiful fish, steel blue to olive green above, shading down the sides to a silvery white on the belly. They have a series of seven or eight horizontal blackish stripes along their sides. There is a faint brassy reflection from the large scales. They grow large. Although the record sport-caught striper in California weighed 78 pounds, the average fish caught weighs less than 10 pounds.

Stripers are anadromous, living a part of their life in the sea and returning each season to spawn in the waters of the delta and the Sacramento and San Joaquin Rivers. In California the stripers spawn in April, May, and June. They do not dig nests in the gravel like trout and salmon, but choose shallow slow moving waters and lay their eggs near the surface. Hundreds of fish, both males and females, in small groups of 10 to 30, mill around near the surface until the eggs are expelled and fertilized.

A five-pound female spawns the first time in her fourth or fifth year. She may lay as many as 250,000 tiny eggs the first year, and later, when she weighs 10 or 12 pounds she may lay as many as 1,000,000 eggs each year. The males may reach sexual maturity when they are two years old and only 11 inches long. After the eggs are fertilized by the sperm of the male, they increase rapidly in size and settle slowly to the bottom. The current

STRIPED BASS

carries them slowly back and forth for two days before the babies hatch.

By July the waters of the San Joaquin River and Suisun Bay literally swarm with small bass. After a year or two they make their way slowly to the bay area and then to the sea. The striper's age, like other fishes, is recorded by the yearly growth rings on their scales. A one-year-old fish is about four inches long. A two-year-old fish 10 inches, a three-year-old fish 15 inches, and by the end of the fourth year it is 19 inches long. They may live for 20 years and attain a length of four feet.

California law prohibits the taking of stripers under 16 inches in length. This gives fish an opportunity to spawn at least once, and, because the striped bass is long lived, most stripers that are not caught one year will be available to be caught the next.

California's striped bass fishery is a valuable resource, from both a recreational and economic standpoint. Over 200,000 anglers fish for stripers in California and catch about 750,000 fish. It has been estimated that the fishermen spend nearly $20,000,000 annually, fishing for stripers. Because of this tremendous value, the Department of Fish and Game works diligently to protect the bass from becoming overfished. Wardens are constantly patrolling the Sacramento and San Joaquin Rivers and the San Francisco Bay regions to enforce the conservation laws, and biologists are continuing their studies to make certain that heavy fishing pressures and water quality do not harm the bass.

The stripers have been introduced into Millerton Lake in Fresno County and into the Colorado River where they are commencing to show in the fishermen's catch. The striper takes baits and lures readily and is excellent eating. Under present management and despite tremendous fishing pressure, the total catch has increased the past few years. All these qualities make the striper a number one game fish, and sport fishermen from all over the west come to the bay area and delta waters to fish for them.

DFG Photo by Jim Ruch

STURGEON

WILDLIFE LEAFLET

State of California
DEPARTMENT OF FISH AND GAME

THIS UNIQUE FISH IS THE LARGEST FRESHWATER FISH IN THE WORLD

The sturgeon is the largest fresh-water fish in the world. There are twenty or more species or subspecies that occur in Asia, northern Europe, and North America. They do not live in the tropics. Seven of these species live in North America, four of which are anadromous (spawn in fresh water but spend a good part of their life at sea). Only the white and the green sturgeon are found on the Pacific Coast. They range from northern California to northwestern Alaska.

The green sturgeon is rarely found in fresh water. It prefers to spend much of its time in the seas and estuaries near the mouths of big rivers. It reaches a length of seven feet and a weight of 350 pounds. The green sturgeon is considered an inferior food fish.

The white sturgeon is the largest fresh-water fish in North America. It is sometimes called the Columbia River, Sacramento, or Pacific sturgeon. It reaches a length of 20 feet and a weight of 1,000 pounds. One specimen weighed 1,900 pounds. Sturgeons grow slowly and live for many years, some reaching 100 years of age. The age is determined by counting the microscopic growth rings on the rays of the pectoral fin. The sturgeons do not look like other fishes. Rows of bony shields or plates partly cover the head and long body. The eyes are small. The mouth is on the underside of the head. The mouth is small but it can be extended, purse like, to suck up small pieces of food. There is a row of four rubbery whiskers or feelers in front of the mouth. The diet of sturgeon living in San Pablo Bay is composed mostly of clams, grass shrimp, mud crabs and herring eggs in that order. When feeding, they root in the mud with their snouts, feeling around with their sensitive whiskers. When food is located the sturgeon protrudes its mouth and sucks the food up from the bottom. There must be a vacuum cleaner action, for rocks, twigs, and other odd items have also been found in its stomach. It is reported that a white sturgeon from the Snake River in Idaho had eaten a half bushel of onions it found floating in the river.

All the sturgeons spawn in fresh water in the spring and early summer. Females are said to spawn for the first time when about 13 to 14 years old, the males a little earlier. At this age they are about three feet long. It appears that an individual fish does not spawn every year, as do most other fish. In California it is illegal to keep a sturgeon less than 40 inches in length. This allows them to spawn at least once before they can be kept. The sturgeons spawn upriver beyond the reach of the tides. They do not build a nest. The eggs are discharged in large grayish masses that cling to vegetation, stones or other material on the bottom. After spawning, both the male and female leave the area and return to the feeding grounds. The eggs hatch in from three to seven days. The baby sturgeon lives the first few days on the egg yolk. When it is about three-quarters of an inch long it commences to eat the minute animal life it finds in the water. It grows rapidly and in a month it is four or five inches long. When it is small it is nearly covered with sharp spines. This gives it good protection. As it grows, the small teeth and spines are shed, and when it is nine inches long it becomes a bottom feeder. It is a strange and wondrous thing that from a half-inch larva the sturgeon can grow to such an enormous size.

In the 1870's white sturgeon 6 to 12 feet long were caught in such numbers that the California markets were flooded. By 1880 the commercial catch had reached 700,000 pounds, but they soon began to disappear. Overfishing, stream pollution, and dams on the rivers and spawning streams took their toll, and in 1901 the season was closed for eight years. The season was reopened in 1910, but in 1917 a complete closure was put into effect until 1954, when sport fishing for sturgeon became legal. It has been so long since sturgeon could be used that the people at first found them strange, but they soon learned that the firm, hard flesh made good eating whether baked, barbecued, boiled, fried, pickled or smoked. The eggs, which look like buckshot, can be made into caviar with a simple process.

This huge white sturgeon was caught in a net by DFG crews during a salmon-tagging program in August of 1955. The brute weighed 462 pounds and contained 87 pounds of eggs. Age was estimated at between 45 and 47 years. The fish was taken at the Fremont Weir in Yolo County. *DFG photo.*

Sport fishermen now regard the sturgeon highly, and, because they are often longer and heavier than the fisherman, landing a big one can test the skill and determination of the best of anglers. Fishing for sturgeon is highly specialized. The sturgeon's slow growth and old age at maturity calls for special regulatory measures in California, both in the methods of fishing and in the minimum size that can be caught.

A continuing tagging and releasing program is being carried on by the Department of Fish and Game in an effort to learn more about this great fish's habits so that it will not once more be endangered by overfishing.

TIMBER RATTLESNAKE

WILDLIFE LEAFLET

State of California
DEPARTMENT OF FISH AND GAME

Throughout the world there are many snakes whose poisonous bite can be fatal to man. In the United States there are four different types, the coral snake, the copperhead snake, the water moccasin and the rattlesnake. The latter is the only poisonous snake native to California.

There are 16 distinct kinds of rattlesnakes. There are numerous subspecies and color variations, but they are all positively identified by the jointed rattles on the tail. Most of the rattlers are concentrated in the southwestern United States. They extend out from there north, east, and south in lessening numbers and kinds, so that every state has one or more kinds. The Pacific rattlesnake is the only rattlesnake found in the Pacific region, north of southern California. In California its range extends south from Oregon to lower California.

In southern California it overlaps the range of several other species and subspecies, except that of the large western diamond rattler that occurs along the Colorado River and southeastern deserts of California. The Pacific rattler is found over a variety of places from seacoast level, inland prairies, and desert areas, to the mountains at elevations of over 10,000 feet.

In favorable areas where there is a constant and abundant supply of small rodents, it sometimes attains a length of five feet, but the average size is between three and four feet. It is more slender than the heavy-bodied diamondbacks of the south and eastern United States. The color and pattern of the markings are varied, ranging from brown to grayish or greenish with large blotches of lighter hues along the back.

In the northern areas of its range and at higher elevations this snake congregates in the fall at crevices in rocky ledges to hibernate for the winter. They return to these places annually. These spots are known as snake dens. In May and early June when outside temperatures begin to warm, the snakes come out of hibernation. They remain around the den entrance for a few days, sunning themselves, and then make their way to the place they spend the summer. They hardly ever go over one mile from their den. Most snakes are secretive in their summer activities, hunting at night and remaining inactive and out of sight for days at a time during the digestive period after eating a squirrel or small rabbit. Consequently more snakes are seen in the spring and fall migrations to and from their winter homes.

Some kinds of snakes lay eggs. In others the eggs are retained in the mother's body until hatched and the young are born alive. Rattlesnakes are among those that give birth to living young. Sometimes a female is killed with the young still in her body. This has given rise to a folk tale that she swallows her babies to protect them from danger. Except for the extreme northern part of California, mating takes place in the spring and the young are born between August and October. The Pacific rattler has from 4 to 25 eggs from which are born an average of 9 or 10 healthy young. The Pacific rattlesnake's babies are about 10 inches long and have one small horny button on the tip of their tail. The babies have venom and short fangs and are dangerous at birth. They are more pugnacious than adults. Although unable to make a rattling sound they throw themselves into a fine defensive pose and strike repeatedly when disturbed. They are completely independent of the mother. They remain in the area of their birth for from 7 to 10 days, at which time they shed their first baby skin and add the first rattle. The litter then commences to break up and start the search for food. Many of the babies do not survive the first year. They die of hunger or are eaten by birds and animals. Even if they make it through the first summer, if they can't find a warm suitable crevice in which to hibernate, they perish the first winter.

If all goes well they grow rapidly. As they grow larger, and each time they come out of hibernation, they shed their skin. Each time they shed their skin a new rattle is added. During the rapid growth of the first few years they may shed their skin three times a year. Thus the number of rattles is not a true indicator of age. The rattles also wear out and break off, so it is unusual to find an adult snake with more than 8 or 10 rattles.

Rattlesnakes eat lizards and small rodents such as ground squirrels, small rabbits, rats and mice. They strike rather than attempt to hold their prey. The fangs are hollow, and when they penetrate the flesh the venom is injected as though from twin hypodermic needles. Much of their small prey is stunned. If a larger animal runs some distance before it dies, they trail it down and swallow it whole.

From Lake Tahoe north on the east side of the Sierra you might see the Great Basin rattler; from

Tahoe south through Death Valley, the sidewinder and Panamint rattlers; along the Colorado River, the western diamondback; in the southwestern area, the red diamondback and speckled rattlers; and in the Mojave Desert, both the Mojave and the sidewinder.

Many persons spend a lifetime hunting, fishing, and picnicking in California and never see a rattlesnake. Few people are bitten. Yet, because the bite is extremely painful and can be fatal, when you are in the field you should always keep alert as to where you step or put your hands. Be careful after dark, for on warm nights rattlesnakes are moving around searching for food.

If you are alone and are struck where the wound can be reached, suck out as much poison as you can in two or three minutes. Then, moving very slowly, seek a cool spot, preferably near water, and remain as quiet as possible. Expect ugly swelling and extreme pain. There are varying degrees in the amount of poison a snake injects. Many people recover without medical aid. Violent exercise, like running or climbing, forces poison through the bloodstream before your system can counteract. Keep the wound cool with wet compresses, leaves, moss, mud or materials at hand. If help is near, get to a doctor as soon as possible, for only a doctor should treat the wound.

Most rattlesnakes when disturbed normally try to withdraw, but if they think they are cornered the explosive sizzling buzz of their rattles is an unmistakable warning and a sound that will long be remembered.

California Wildlife Information Sheet

The Resources Agency of California—Department of Fish and Game

Tree Squirrel

There are three different species of tree dwelling squirrels within the forests of California's mountains, and in the oak woodland areas of the foothills and valleys. They are the gray squirrel, the little Douglas squirrel or chickaree, and the nocturnal flying squirrel. They are the only tree squirrels in California except the eastern red squirrel that was introduced into some of the city parks and has since spread into some of the central coast counties.

The gray squirrel is the largest, being nearly two feet from the tip of its nose to the end of its long bushy tail. Its coat and tail are clear gray with white on the underparts of the body. It lives both in the forests of the mountains and in the oak woodland areas in the valleys and foothills.

On the ground gray squirrels appear leisurely and graceful but if danger is present they climb and run through the treetops with ease. They make their homes in hollows in the trees and sometimes make a shallow nest of twigs on a limb 30 feet or so above the ground. The breeding season extends from January through July. They have from three to five babies in a litter and sometimes two litters a year. The babies are born blind and helpless, and are nearly six weeks old before they are ready to leave the nest. They spend considerable time on the ground foraging for food. They eat mushrooms, acorns, pine nuts, and grain if it is available. They store a large amount of their food. Recent studies in northern California show that subterranean mushrooms or "fake" truffles, which they dig beneath the trees, make up over one half of their diet.

The little Douglas squirrel or chickaree is much more active than its larger cousin the gray squirrel. It lives at higher elevations in the pine forests. These animals are curious, noisy, and active. Their chattering call, accompanied by a series of explosive little grunts, growls, and clucks, attracts quick attention. The Douglas squirrels' day begins early! At sunrise they will be 200 feet high in a tree cutting pine cones which they store in great quantities. Pine nuts are their favorite food. The husked cones are found in neat piles near the base of a tree or rock. They also eat animal food such as nestlings, bird eggs, and some insects. They live in old woodpecker holes and hollow limbs in trees high above the ground. A litter of four is born in the spring. In California the Douglas squirrel is seldom hunted as a game animal, even though there is an open season.

The smallest of the California tree squirrels is the flying squirrel. Its coat is a soft gray with cream colored underparts. Its tail is flattened and is the same color as the back. Like other strictly nocturnal animals, its eyes are large and its whiskers are long. The most interesting difference about the flying squirrel is the soft furry membrane that connects its front and hind feet. When they spread their legs and tails they are about five or six inches square and quite flat. This enables them to glide for long distances.

Because they are seldom seen, few people realize that they are quite common in California's forests. However, after sundown if you were to sit quietly around a camp in the woods, you could hear them scrambling around in the tall trees. These little squirrels are extremely fast climbers. They leave one tree by gliding as far as 100 feet to reach a spot at a lower elevation. They land with an audible thump and then climb to a higher elevation to glide again, veering upwards to alight. Vocal sounds are small and birdlike, and when they are in distress, they emit a shrill squeal.

They also spend a good deal of their time foraging on the ground. They eat nuts, berries, insects, and some fungi. They also like meat, and feed on any carcasses they might find. They live in old woodpecker holes and natural cavities in the trees and also make a shallow twig nest on a limb. The breeding season is in late winter. They have from two to six pink hairless babies in a litter, and sometimes there are two litters per year. The eyes of the babies are closed and the gliding membranes are transparent. Their eyes open in 28 days and they are weaned at five weeks. If the nest is endangered the mother will move the babies by holding them firmly in her teeth and gliding to safety. The young can make short glides in eight weeks.

None of the tree squirrels hibernate, although they remain inactive during the coldest weather.

California's tree squirrels are protected except for a carefully limited open season. Some hunters, particularly those from eastern states, enjoy hunting squirrels, and the big gray squirrel is an exciting quarry and provides excellent fare for the supper table.

WILD PIG

WILDLIFE
LEAFLET

State of California
DEPARTMENT OF FISH AND GAME

SPORTSMEN SHOW INCREASING INTEREST IN THE EUROPEAN WILD PIG

In California the European wild pig is a minor big game species but one in which the sportsmen of the state are showing an increasing interest.

The European wild pig is long legged, compared to domestic pigs, and reaches a length of about five feet. The adults may reach a height of two to three feet at the shoulder, tapering off toward the hind legs. Adult boars may weigh up to 600 pounds, but a 300-pound boar and a 200-pound sow are large in California. The boar pictured by the overturned garbage weighed 347 pounds.

In its native Europe, the wild pig is covered with bristly hairs under which is a fine woolly undercoat. The European wild pig in California does not possess this undercoat, possibly as the result of feral pig interbreeding and lack of extensive winter snow. Its color varies from pale gray to black in adults. The animal has erect, hairy ears and a naked snout. The canine tusks that protrude from its mouth have been known to exceed 11 inches in length in Europe. In California, normal tusks are rarely over three inches long. These tusks are used for rooting and fighting and may be razor sharp.

The wild pig is capable of considerable speed for short distances. Ordinarily wary, it will nonetheless fight fearlessly and is considered among the most dangerous of wild animals when wounded, cornered, or encountered with small young.

The wild pig has very poor sight, but its senses

of hearing and of smell are very acute. An elusive animal, the boar leads a solitary life, disdaining the company of other wild pigs except at breeding time. Several sows with pigs often gather together in bands, however. The rutting season occurs toward the end of the year in Monterey County, and piglets are born about four months later. Occasionally sows will produce two litters in a year. So it is not unusual to see little pigs in varying sizes at any season. The sow has a strong motherly instinct and will fight savagely to protect her young.

There may be from 6 to 12 little pigs in a litter. The young, like all babies, are cute. They are dark brown with light rusty stripes running the length of the body. The coloration serves as camouflage and makes them difficult to observe in the broken shadows of their daytime hideaway. When they are about six months old, the stripes disappear.

The European wild pig and its crosses with domestic pig tend to be more nocturnal than feral pigs (domestic pigs gone wild). During the daytime they stay fairly well hidden, but will feed in the early morning and late evening. They root up the ground in obtaining bulbs, mushrooms, insects, plant roots, acorns and miscellaneous low-growing plants. They also are scavengers, eating dead carcasses and offal.

Wherever found around the world, the wild pig is notorious for its extensive and severe damage to ground crops. It is extremely difficult to bring under control. Serious consideration of this factor should precede introduction of the animal to new areas.

The European wild pig was reportedly introduced from Europe into North Carolina in 1910. In 1920, it escaped into the wild. It is believed that there was some mixing with domestic pigs at that time. It now occurs abundantly in Tennessee and is found in New Hampshire. In 1925, the progeny of the North Carolina imports were shipped into Carmel Valley in Monterey County, California, where they were released in the wild in late 1925 or early 1926. They spread into the Santa Lucia Mountain range and may now be found in the rugged area south and west of the Carmel River, in the northern portion of Los Padres National Forest, and in the rugged country just west of King City. The range of our purist strain of European wild pig is limited in California although the feral pig is common in many areas. In the wild, the domestic pig quickly reverts to a razor back type and becomes similar to the European wild pig in most respects, except that it tends to feed more throughout the day.

It has been estimated recently that there are approximately 3,000 European wild pigs in California with an accompanying population of 5,000 wild domestic pigs on the mainland and 5,000 plus wild domestic pigs on the offshore islands of Santa Catalina and Santa Cruz. Many of these are found on private land. In areas where there is no conflict with agriculture or recreation, they have been an interesting addition to California wildlife and a challenge to both the gun and bow hunter.

California Wildlife Information Sheet

The Resources Agency of California—Department of Fish and Game

Wild Turkey

The wild turkey is the largest land bird in North America and native only to this continent. It was found originally by the early settlers in the wooded areas of eastern and southeastern United States and the semiarid brush and woodland areas of southwestern United States and Mexico. Since its first use by the Pilgrim fathers, the turkey has been a symbol of thanksgiving and has been prized as a game bird by hunters.

Turkeys abounded in early times, but unrestricted hunting for the market caused the birds to become so scarce that soon after 1880 laws were passed banning the sale of wild turkeys.

The wild turkey was not native to California, but because of its great desirability the Department of Fish and Game began turkey introductions into California in 1908. The birds released in California since that time have come from Mexico, Arizona, Texas and state game farms. They have been planted in 71 different sites in 23 counties.

By continuous study and experimenting with different varieties, the wild turkey is now well established in the Cloverdale area—Sonoma County; Castro Valley—Santa Clara County; Adelaide district—San Luis Obispo County; and the Brush Creek area in Tulare County. The range of the turkey in California is being extended by trapping and transplanting wild birds from these areas.

The wild turkey is similar in appearance to the domestic turkey that we know today, except the coloring is more brilliant. It is a large bird. The males are called toms or gobblers. A large gobbler may weigh 20 pounds. Despite its size, the turkey is a perching bird, and good roosting sites 30–40 feet above the ground play an important part in the turkeys choice of a place to live. They use the same roosting place until continuous harassment drives them away. Wild turkeys are extremely wary and are difficult to approach.

The mating season begins in February and lasts through June. The gobbler does not choose a single hen for a mate. He picks out a little clearing for a strutting ground, and early each morning gobbles and struts to attract the hens. During this time the gobbler throws caution to the winds in an effort to attract the hens. Fanning his tail, spreading his wings down till the tips scrape the ground, and fluffing his feathers so the sun's rays reflect the iridescent colors, he makes a magnificent display before he chooses a mate.

While the hen is nesting she is very secretive. Choosing a place near water she hides her nest on the ground, and slips into and away from it with great stealth. She lays from 5 to 17 buff-colored eggs that are pointed on one end, and sprinkled all over with little brown flecks.

It takes 28 days for the eggs to hatch. Near hatching time she will remain on the nest despite the grave danger.

WILD TURKEYS

Baby turkeys are called poults. The babies are a downy yellowish brown and unlike most birds the wing feathers are prominent from the beginning. As soon as the poults are dry and the weather is nice the mother takes them on a search for food. They eat insects and the green leaves of many plants. When they are 1½ months old they can make short flights, and at four months they moult and gradually change to adult plumage. As they grow older they prefer grasshoppers, berries, the seeds of grasses, and acorns, which they swallow whole.

Turkeys prefer to live in flocks. This may be for the added protection from danger; for, from the time they are born, the entire flock, even adult birds, lives in obedience to the danger call regardless of which turkey makes it. It is fascinating to watch them run and hide, even if the alarm given was false.

The turkey's importance as a game bird in California will probably be judged on quality rather than quantity. It is considered by many to be the finest tasting of all game birds. This, plus its size and its increasing wariness of man, has made it a trophy that tests the ability of the most patient and skillful hunter and has caused it to become one of the most highly prized game birds in North America.

If the turkey continues to thrive in California, it will be another example of the department's successful efforts to introduce a species in game deficient areas, and management plans will probably include limited hunting.

DFG Photo by A. E. Naylor

WOOD DUCK

WILDLIFE LEAFLET

State of California
DEPARTMENT OF FISH AND GAME

WOOD DUCKS ARE AMONG THE MOST BEAUTIFUL OF OUR NORTH AMERICAN BIRDS

The male wood duck is one of the most beautiful of our North American birds. The rich greens, blues, and burgundy body colors are sharply contrasted by bold white markings. The head is crested with iridescent greens and purples, and the red eyes and red-orange bill are further accented by white patches on the throat. The drake was sought by early day market hunters who found a ready sale for the strikingly beautiful plumage.

The hen is a little smaller than the drake; her plumage, although brighter than other hen ducks, is not as colorful as the drake.

The wood duck, unlike most other ducks, does not seek open water in which to live. It prefers wooded lakes and streams, and it builds its nest in cavities in the limbs and trunks of trees, rather than on the ground. It seems to prefer trees that are near the water, although it does nest as much as a mile from water. It readily uses artificial nesting boxes if they have been suitably placed.

The hen and drake search for a nest site together. If a likely looking cavity is found, the drake will roost nearby while the hen inspects it for a possible nest. Everything must be just so, and she may spend from five minutes to an hour before she decides if the cavity will be suitable.

The hen does not carry any materials for nest building. She merely hollows out a depression in the bottom of the cavity and commences to lay. After several days, she starts to cover the eggs with down and soft feathers, which she plucks from her breast.

In a normal nest the hen lays from 10 to 15 smooth white eggs. Sometimes if nesting sites are scarce, more than one hen will lay in the same nest. As many as 43 eggs have been found. These are called dump nests and are seldom successful.

After a clutch of eggs has been laid, the hen starts to set or incubate the eggs. It takes from 28 to 31 days for the eggs to hatch. Mallard duck eggs hatch in approximately 22 to 24 days. The hen only leaves the nest for an hour or so at dawn and again at dusk. The time is spent with the drake, who stays nearby until the last few days before the eggs hatch. He then deserts the area, and the hen has the full responsibility of rearing the brood.

The morning after all the eggs have hatched the mother flies down to the water or to the ground and after checking carefully to see that there is no danger, calls the young from the nest. The baby wood ducks have very sharp toenails that enable them to clamber up the straight sides of the nest cavity, sometimes several feet, and without hesitation fling themselves

into space where they fall to the ground or to the water. They are rarely injured. Occasionally a weak duckling fails to mount the nest wall and dies of exhaustion within the nest cavity. When the hen is certain no more babies are coming, she collects them with a soft call and starts for water. Some may be lost if they are too far from water.

Once on the water, they are fairly safe. It takes them nearly two months to grow large enough to fly. When they are small they live on insects and the tender leaves found at the water's edge, but as they grow older and learn to fly, they go inland for berries, grapes, and acorns, which they swallow whole. They eat a great variety of vegetable matter.

The wood duck rests in open pools at night; flying out to feed by day. After they have fed, they seek out quiet stretches of wooded streams or canals and roost along the banks and on the limbs of trees. The day is spent visiting and preening themselves, seemingly content, but always alert to danger. If alarmed, they burst into the air with a distinctive squealing cry of danger.

The greatest population of wood ducks in the United States is from the upper Mississippi River eastward through New England. A smaller group inhabits the West Coast from central California to southern British Columbia.

In California the summer wood duck population is distributed sparsely over most of the state north of the Tehachapi Mountains. The winter migrations of the resident population amount to a shift out of the higher elevations into the central valleys and adjoining foothills, where they are joined by the bulk of the wood ducks in the Pacific flyway that migrate from Oregon, Washington, and British Columbia to winter in California.

The wood duck has probably suffered more from the effects of civilization than other ducks. By the early 1900's the combined effects of overshooting and habitat destruction had depleted their numbers to a point where conservationists were concerned that they might become extinct. In 1918 Congress gave the wood duck complete protection from hunting till 1941 when one bird was allowed in the hunter's bag.

Overshooting, however, was not the most important reason for the decline in the wood duck population. Of more importance was the draining of marshes and the cutting of the oaks, sycamore and willows, along the rivers and streams. These trees furnished the kinds of cavities that were preferred nesting sites of the wood duck. This peculiar habit or nesting requirement led to the development of artificial nesting boxes which are now used extensively throughout the United States, and has contributed materially to maintaining a population of these beautiful birds that are enjoyed by hunters and nature lovers alike.

For detailed instructions on the building and installation of artificial wood duck nesting boxes, please contact the California Department of Fish and Game.

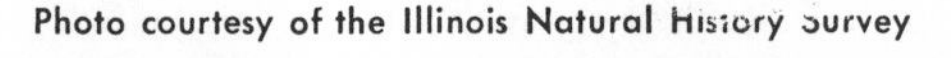

Photo courtesy of the Illinois Natural History Survey

COM